VICTOR VASARELY *Meandre,* 1951. Aubusson tapestry, 9 × 7½ ft.
Courtesy of the Feigen Gallery.

SOME HAYSTACKS
DON'T EVEN
HAVE ANY NEEDLE

And Other Complete Modern Poems

Compiled

by

Stephen Dunning

Edward Lueders

Hugh Smith

SOME HAYSTACKS
DON'T EVEN
HAVE ANY NEEDLE

And Other Complete Modern Poems

Stephen Dunning

Edward Lueders

Hugh Smith

Editorial Direction: **Leo Kneer**

Development: **Nora Rotzoll,**
      Philip Brantingham, Ronald Mochel

Design: **Don Marvine**

**Lothrop, Lee & Shepard Co.
New York**

Picture Credits

DALI, SALVADOR

84 *Portrait of My Dead Brother.*
Courtesy of
M. Knoedler & Co., Inc.

DE KOONING, WILLEM

80 Detail from *Woman VI.*
Museum of Art, Carnegie
Institute, Pittsburgh.

DUBUFFET, JEAN

32 *Smoker by a Wall.*
Collection of
Julian J. and Joachim Jean
Aberbach, New York.
49 *Mirandoliana.*
Collection of
Mr. and Mrs. Sam Zacks,
Toronto.
121 *The Cow with the Subtile Nose.*
1954. Oil and duco on canvas,
35 x 45¾''. Collection, The
Museum of Modern Art, New
York. Benjamin Scharps and
David Scharps Fund.

GATCH, LEE

68 *Industrial Night.*
The Phillips Collection,
Washington.

GIULIANI, VIN

88 *Assemblage.*

GOTTLIEB, ADOLPH

103 *Burst.*
Collection of
Mr. and Mrs. Ben Heller,
New York.

GRAVES, MORRIS

159 *Wounded Scoter II.*
The Cleveland Museum of Art,
Gift of Gamblers in Modern
Art.

174 *Joyous Young Pine.* (1944).
Watercolor and gouache, 53⅝
x 27''. Collection, The Museum
of Modern Art, New York.
Purchase.

HARRIS, PAUL

56 *Seated Figure.*
Photo by Jon Brenneis
for TIME.

HOPPER, EDWARD

171 *Rooms by the Sea.*
Yale University Art Gallery,
Bequest of Stephen Carlton
Clark, B.A. 1903.

HUNT, RICHARD

76 *Winged Fragment.*
Courtesy of
Mr. and Mrs. David Hoffman.

KIENHOLZ, EDWARD

154 *Ida Franger.*
Courtesy of
Mr. and Mrs James Butler,
Los Angeles.

KLEE, PAUL

61 *A Guardian Angel Serves a
Little Breakfast.* 1920.
Courtesy of Felix Klee.
64 *Actor's Mask* (Schauspielermaske). 1924. Oil on canvas
mounted on board, 14⅜ ×
14⅜''. Sidney and Harriet Janis
Collection. Gift to The Museum of Modern Art. New York.
124 *The Seafarer.*
Courtesy of
Frau Trix Dürst-Haass.

MASSON, ANDRÉ

113 *Divertissements d'été.*
Private collection, France.

Permission A.D.A.G.P. 1968 by
French Reproduction Rights,
Inc.

MATISSE, HENRI

28 *Le Lagon.*
Courtesy of The Art Institute of
Chicago. Permission SPADEM
1968 by French Reproduction
Rights, Inc.

MIRO, JOAN

20 *Dancer Listening to the Organ
in a Gothic Cathedral.*
Permission A.D.A.G.P. 1968 by
French Reproduction Rights,
Inc.
187 *Dog Barking at the Moon.*
1926. Philadelphia Museum of
Art, A.E. Gallatin Collection.

O'KEEFFE, GEORGIA

135 *Cow's Skull: Red, White, &
Blue.* Courtesy of the Metro-
politan Museum of Art, The
Alfred Stieglitz Collection,
1949.

PHILLIPS, PETER

38 *Custom Painting No. 3.*
American Republic Insurance
Company, Des Moines, Iowa.

REDON, ODILON

111 *The Spider.*
Courtesy of
The Art Institute of Chicago.

VASARELY, VICTOR

Cover *Meandre.*
Courtesy of
the Feigen Gallery, Chicago.

Acknowledgments

"All in The Path of a Power Mower" by Richard Gillman, from *The Beloit Poetry Journal* (Spring, 1961). Reprinted by permission of *The Beloit Poetry Journal*. "Ape" from "Creatures in the Zoo" by Babette Deutsch, from COMING OF AGE. Published by Indiana University Press. Reprinted by permission of the author. "Apostrophe to Man" from COLLECTED POEMS, Harper & Row. Copyright 1934, © 1962 by Edna St. Vincent Millay and Norma Millay Ellis. "Art Review" by Kenneth Fearing from NEW AND SELECTED POEMS. Reprinted by permission of the publisher, Indiana University Press. "At the Airport" from THE BLUE SWALLOWS by Howard Nemerov. Copyright © 1967 by Howard Nemerov. Published by the University of Chicago Press. Originally appeared in *The New Yorker* (November, 1966). Reprinted by permission of Margot Johnson Agency. "The Aura" Copyright © 1965 by James Dickey. Reprinted from POEMS 1957-1967, by James Dickey, by permission of Wesleyan University Press and Rapp & Whiting Limited, 76 New Oxford Street, London WC1, England. Originally published in *The New Yorker*.

"The Bagel" Copyright © 1966 by David Ignatow. Reprinted from RESCUE THE DEAD, (British title: EARTH HARD) by David Ignatow, by permission of Wesleyan University Press and Rapp & Whiting Limited. "Bats" Reprinted with permission of The Macmillan Company from THE BAT-POET by Randall Jarrell. Copyright © The Macmillan Company 1963, 1964. The following poem is reprinted with the permission of Charles Scribner's Sons: "The Battle" from GOOD NEWS OF DEATH AND OTHER POEMS (Copyright 1955 Louis Simpson) by Louis Simpson, POETS OF TODAY II. "The Bicycle" by Jerzy Harasymowicz, translated by Edmund Ordon from SAN FRANCISCO REVIEW ANNUAL #1. Reprinted by permission of San Francisco Review. "A Blessing" Copyright © 1961 by James Wright. Reprinted from THE BRANCH WILL NOT BREAK, by James Wright, by permission of Wesleyan University Press and Longmans, Green & Co. Limited. This poem was first published in Poetry Magazine. "Brazilian Happenings" by Richard O'Connell. Reprinted by permission; © 1966 The New Yorker Magazine, Inc. "The Brothers: Two Saltimbanques" by John Logan from GHOSTS OF THE HEART. Copyright © 1960 by John Logan. Published by The University of Chicago Press. Reprinted by permission of the author. "By The Swimming" by Robert Sward from KISSING THE DANCER & OTHER POEMS. Copyright © 1964 by Robert Sward. Published by Cornell University Press. Reprinted by permission of the author.

"The Centaur" (Copyright © 1956 May Swenson) is reprinted with the permission of Charles Scribner's Sons from TO MIX WITH TIME by May Swenson. "A Certain Age" from TIMES THREE by Phyllis McGinley. Copyright 1956 by Phyllis McGinley. Originally appeared in *The New Yorker*. Reprinted by permission of The Viking Press, Inc. and Martin Secker & Warburg Limited. "Child With Malaria" by Clark Mills from "Speech After Darkness" in FIVE YOUNG AMERICAN POETS. Copyright 1941 by New Directions. Reprinted by permission of New Directions Publishing Corporation. "The Chums," copyright © 1963

9

Table of Contents

Foreword

Our first question in considering any poem for this book was whether it can speak *now* to readers willing to give some time to it.

We selected poems with fresh images, for one thing—images from today's world. These poems use contemporary language, for another—words, phrases, entire poems have the sound of the talk we hear around us. The old themes such as love and loneliness, anger and compassion are here. But they are set in the context of now, a now which is often wild, zany, tense, tender, stark, violent. Finally, the poems here are formed or shaped in a rich variety of ways. Some of them look the way poems have looked for a long time. Others don't; they move around on the page, mix long lines with short, and insist that readers pay attention to their rhythms and silences. Some use rhyme while others do not; but they all have music and sound systems.

These poems are meant to be heard as well as seen.

JOAN MIRO *Dancer Listening to the Organ in a Gothic Cathedral*

AN EASY DECISION

I had finished my dinner
Gone for a walk
It was fine
Out and I started whistling

It wasn't long before

I met a
Man and his wife riding on
A pony with seven

Kids running along beside them

I said hello and

Went on
Pretty soon I met another
Couple
This time with nineteen
Kids and all of them
Riding on
A big smiling hippopotamus

I invited them home

Kenneth Patchen

THE BICYCLE

once
forgotten by tourists
a bicycle joined
a herd
of mountain goats

with its splendidly turned
silver horns
it became
their leader

with its bell
it warned them
of danger

with them
it partook
in romps
on the snow covered
glade

the bicycle
gazed from above
on people walking;
with the goats

it fought
over a goat,
with a bearded buck

it reared up at eagles
enraged
on its back wheel

it was happy
though it never
nibbled at grass

or drank
from a stream

until once
a poacher
shot it

tempted
by the silver trophy
of its horns

and then
above the Tatras was seen
against the sparkling
January sky

the angel of death erect
slowly
riding to heaven
holding the bicycle's
dead horns.

Jerzy Harasymowicz

*(Trans. from the Polish
by Edmund Ordon)*

THE BAGEL   **by David Ignatow**

I stopped to pick up the bagel
rolling away in the wind,
annoyed with myself
for having dropped it
as it were a portent.
Faster and faster it rolled,
with me running after it
bent low, gritting my teeth,
and found myself doubled over
and rolling down the street
head over heels, one complete somersault
after another like a bagel
and strangely happy with myself.

THE STONE

by
Paul
Blackburn

The stone found me in bright sunlight
around 9th and Stuyvesant Streets and
found, if not a friend, at
least a travelling companion.
Kicking, we crossed
Third Avenue, then Cooper Square, a-
voiding the traffic in our oblique and
random way, a cab almost got him, and I had
to wait a few seconds, crowding
in from the triangular portion edged about
with signs, safety island, crossed
Lafayette, him catching between the cobbles, then
with a judicious blow
from the toes of my foot (right), well, a
soccer kick aiming for height, we cleared
the curb and turned left down Lafayette,
that long block,
with a wide sidewalk and plenty of room to maneuver
in over metal cellar doorways or swinging
out toward the curb edge. The low worn
curb at 4th was a cinch to make, and
at Great Jones Street the driveway into a
gas station promised no impediment. But
then he rolled suddenly to the right
as though following an old gentleman in a long
coat, and at the same time I was addressed
by a painter I know and his girl on their way
to Washington Square, and as I looked up to
answer,

I heard the small sound. He had fallen
in his run, into water gathered in a sunken
plate which they lift to tighten or loosen
something to do with the city water supply I think,
and sank out of sight.
I spoke to Simeon and Dee
about a loft it turned out he hadn't gotten, but
felt so desolate at having lost him they didn't
stay long, I looked at the puddle, explained
we'd come all the way from beyond Cooper Square,
they hurried away.
I suppose I could have used my hands, picked him
out and continued, he'd have been dry by the time
we got home, but just as I decided to abandon him
the sun disappeared.
I continued on down Bleecker finally,
a warm front moving in from the west, the
cirrus clotting into alto-cumulus, sun seeping through
as the front thickened, but not shining, the air turned
cool, and there were pigeons
circling
over the buildings at
West Broadway, and over them a gull, a
young man with a beard and torn army jacket walked
a big mutt on a short leash teaching him to heel.
The mutt was fine, trotting alongside, nuzzling
lightly at his master's chino pants, the young
man smiled, the dog smiled too, and on they went.
They had each other.
I had left him there in the puddle, our game
over, no fair using hands I had told myself.
Not that he could have smiled.
The sun gone in.
He had been shaped like a drunken pyramid, ir-
regularly triangular.
I liked him.

REGARDING
A
DOOR

by
David Antin

regarding a door
its open and shut
but it is less open and shut than a wall
a wall is something to lean on
and its unwise to lean on a door
regarding a door
you can take it in hand
turning the knob of a door you can open it and step through
then its no longer a door
now in the case of a wall
its a wall wherever you are
which is evident and consoling
with a wall you always know where you are
while a door is only a door from outside
there is also something substantial about walls
maybe its the materials from which theyre made
the bricks and the plaster
but more likely its the absence of hinges
the hinges in doors are like hidden conditions
upon which everything turns
theyre like the small print in contracts
a door depends on its hinges

but it also depends on a wall
there is nothing unusual about a wall without doors
a door without a wall is ridiculous
also a door is usually visible in all of its limits
but you cannot see the other side of a wall
and a door is always suggesting another side
so doors seem ambiguous and appear to be forever flapping in the wind
a revolving door seems to be always changing its mind
but regarded from whatever angle
it is always offering you the same proposition
there are many unanswered questions about doors
why is it that there arent circular or elliptical doors
what is it thats frightening about sliding doors
and what about the colors of doors
green doors in brick walls
white doors in black walls
or black doors in any walls
this will lead you to suspect that i am talking about symbols
rather than about doors and walls
whats all this talk about doors and walls anyway
why not talk about something real
like strainers

Section

2

LITERATURE:

THE GOD,

ITS RITUAL

by

Merrill

Moore

Something strange I do not comprehend
Is this: I start to write a certain verse
But by the time that I come to its end
Another has been written that is worse
Or possibly better than the one I meant,
And certainly not the same, and different.

I cannot understand it—I begin
A poem and then it changes as I write,
Never have I written the one I thought I might,
Never gone out the door that I came in,
Until I am perplexed by this perverse
Manner and behavior of my verse.

I've never written the poem that I intended;
The poem was always different when it ended.

POEM TO BE READ AT   3 A.M.   by Donald Justice

Excepting the diner
On the outskirts
The town of Ladora
At 3 A.M.
Was dark but
For my headlights
And up in
One second-story room
A single light
Where someone
Was sick or
Perhaps reading
As I drove past
At seventy
Not thinking
This poem
Is for whoever
Had the light on

Wind, bird, and tree,
Water, grass, and light:
In half of what I write
Roughly or smoothly
Year by impatient year,
The same six words recur.

I have as many floors
As meadows or rivers,
As much still air as wind
And as many cats in mind
As nests in the branches
To put an end to these.

THE WORDS   by David Wagoner

Instead, I take what is:
The light beats on the stones,
And wind over water shines
Like long grass through the trees,
As I set loose, like birds
In a landscape, the old words.

THE

MAPMAKER

ON

HIS

ART

by

Howard

Nemerov

After the bronzed, heroic traveller
Returns to the television interview
And cocktails at the Ritz, I, in my turn,
Set forth across the clean, uncharted paper.
Smiling a little at his encounters with
Savages, bugs, and snakes, for the most part
Skipping his night thoughts, philosophic notes,
Rainy reflections, I translate his trip
Into my native tongue of bearings, shapes,
Directions, distances. My fluent pen
Wanders and cranks as his great river does,
Over the page, making the lonely voyage
Common and human. This, my modest art,
Brings wilderness well down into the range
Of any budget. Under the haunted mountain
Where he lay in delirium, deserted
By his safari, they will build hotels
In a year or two. I make no claim that this
Much matters (they will name a hotel for him,
Not me), yet, lest in the comparison
I should appear a trifle colorless,
I write the running river a rich blue
And—let imagination rage!—wild green
The jungles with their tawny meadows and swamps
Where, till the day I die, I will not go.

JEAN DUBUFFET *Smoker by a Wall*

ART

REVIEW

Recently displayed at the Times Square Station, a new Vandyke on the face-cream girl.
(Artist unknown. Has promise, but lacks the brilliance shown by the great masters
      of the Elevated age)
The latest wood carving in a Whelan telephone booth, titled "O Mortal Fools WA 9-5090,"
      shows two winged hearts above an ace of spades.
(His meaning is not entirely clear, but this man will go far)
A charcoal nude in the rear of Flatbush Ahearn's Bar & Grill, "Forward to the
      Brotherhood of Man," has been boldly conceived in the great tradition.
(We need more, much more of this)
Then there is the chalk portrait, on the walls of a waterfront warehouse, of a
      gentleman wearing a derby hat: "Bleecker Street Mike is a double-crossing rat."
(Morbid, but powerful. Don't miss)

Know then by these presents, know all men by these signs and omens, by these simple
      thumbprints on the throat of time,
Know that Pete, the people's artist, is ever watchful,
That Tuxedo Jim has passed among us, and was much displeased, as always,
That George the Ghost (no man has ever seen him) and Billy the Bicep boy will neither
      bend nor break,
That Mr. Harkness of Sunnyside still hopes for the best, and has not lost his
      human touch,
That Phantom Phil, the master of them all, has come and gone, but will return, and
      all is well.

Kenneth   Fearing

UNGAINLY THINGS   by Robert Wallace

A regular country toad—pebbly,
    squat,
        shadow-green

as the shade of the spruces
    in the garden
        he came from—rode

to Paris in a hatbox,
    to Lautrec's
        studio (skylights

on the skies of Paris)
    and stared
        from searchlight eyes,

dim yellow; bow-armed,
    ate
        cut-worms from a box,

hopped
    occasionally
        among the furniture and easels,

while the clumsy little painter
        studied
                him in charcoal

until he was beautiful.
        One day
                he found his way

down stairs toward the world
        again,
                into the streets of Montmartre,

and, missing him, the painter-dwarf
        followed,
                peering among the cobbles,

laughed at, searching
        until long past dark
                the length of the Avenue Frochot,

over and over,
        for the fisted, marble-eyed
                fellow

no one would ever see again
        except in sketches
                that make ungainly things beautiful.

FROM

A

19TH CENTURY

KANSAS

PAINTER'S

NOTEBOOK

I always paint pictures
of violent weather
(mostly tornadoes
with thick dragon tails
that strike like snakes),
then give them away
to queasy aunts
and quaking uncles.
Though I find peace
in strawberry sunsets,
and those May wine days
when a clover breeze
ding-dongs the tulips,
I am obsessed
with steep funnel-shaped clouds
and frightened children
who cry and run scared
through towering cornfields.
I paint only
the dark-stained pictures

by Dave Etter   that storm in my head.

YOUR POEM, MAN . . .

unless there's one thing seen
suddenly against another—a parsnip
sprouting for a President, or
hailstones melting in an ashtray—
nothing really happens. It takes
surprise and wild connections,
doesn't it? A walrus chewing
on a ballpoint pen. Two blue tail-
lights on Tyrannosaurus Rex. Green
cheese teeth. Maybe what we wanted
least. Or most. Some unexpected
pleats. Words that never knew
each other till right now. Plug us
into the wrong socket and see
what blows—or what lights up.
Try
     untried
         circuitry,
new
     fuses.
Tell it like it never really was,
man,
and maybe we can see it
like it is.

Edward Lueders

PETER PHILLIPS *Custom Painting No. 3*

Section 3

CORNER   by Ralph Pomeroy

The cop slumps alertly on his motorcycle,
Supported by one leg like a leather stork.
His glance accuses me of loitering.
I can see his eyes moving like a fish
In the green depths of his green goggles.

His ease is fake. I can tell.
My ease is fake. And he can tell.
The fingers armored by his gloves
Splay and clench, itching to change
                        something.
As if he were my enemy or my death,
I just standing there watching.

I spit out my gum which has gone stale.
I knock out a new cigarette—
Which is my bravery.
It is all imperceptible:
The way I shift my weight,
The way he creaks in his saddle.

The traffic is specific though constant.
The sun surrounds me, divides the street between us.
His crash helmet is whiter in the shade.
It is like a bull ring as they say it is just before the
                                            fighting.

I cannot back down. I am there.

Everything holds me back.
I am in danger of disappearing into the sunny dust.
My levis bake and my T shirt sweats.

My cigarette makes my eyes burn.
But I don't dare drop it.

Who made him my enemy?
Prince of coolness. King of fear.
Why do I lean here waiting?
Why does he lounge there watching?

I am becoming sunlight.
My hair is on fire. My boots run like tar.
I am hung-up by the bright air.

Something breaks through all of a sudden,
And he blasts off, quick as a craver,
Smug in his power; watching me watch.

GROWING UP

A big Jack, cutting outward toward blue,
little puffs of my bullets hurrying him.
Sage crushed underfoot, crisp & clean—

My father, a big Irishman, redfaced & watching,
he who could hit anything within range,
who brought a 150-lb buck three miles
out of the high mountains when he was 57

—a man who counted misses as weaknesses,
  he whipped up his own rifle, stopped the Jack
  folding him in midair, glanced at me, stood
  silent

My father who never knew I shot pips from cards
candleflames out (his own eye) who would've
been shamed by a son who couldn't kill. Riding
beside him.

Keith Wilson

REEL ONE

It was all technicolor
from bullets to nurses.
The guns gleamed like cars
and blood was as red
as the paint on dancers.
The screen shook with fire
and my bones whistled.
It was like life, but better.

I held my girl's hand,
in the deepest parts,
and we walked home, after,
with the snow falling,
but there wasn't much blue
in the drifts or corners:
just white and more white
and the sound track so dead
you could almost imagine
the trees were talking.

Adrien Stoutenburg

THE CHUMS

Some are in prison; some are dead;
    And none has read my books,
And yet my thought turns back to them,
    And I remember looks

Their sisters gave me, once or twice;
    But when I slowed my feet,
They taught me not to be too nice
    The way I tipped my hat.

And when I slipped upon the ice,
They saw that I fell more than twice.
    I'm grateful for that.

Theodore Roethke

MODIFICATIONS
by Ron Koertge

When I was young and we were poor and I used to
gripe about the food, my mother would say
"Eat what's in front of you and be thankful you

ain't worse off." That didn't make much of an
impression then and after I left home I didn't
think any more about it except to make fun,

you know how that goes. Then a few months ago
I had a lot of trouble, nothing that most
people couldn't handle but I'm not most people

and it wigged me out all but for good. The
only way I held my junk-shop life together was
by remembering all the good old rules: So now

I honor my father and mother like crazy, go to
bed really early, take hundreds of stitches
in time but most of all I eat what's put in front

of me. Lately I've eaten a lot of forks and
things and right now there's a nice waitress in the
hospital just because she didn't move her hand in

time. It's too bad but I've just got to have the
rules to keep my arms and legs from flying off, so
whenever I sit down I think them over and chew 50

times and say thank you thank you thank you thank
you thank you thank you thank you thank you thank
you thank you thank you thank you thank you.

That junkyard fell down the side of the hill
like a river: baby buggy, black leather
cracked car back seat, sofa wind-siphoned
by a clutch of tangled wire hangers hanging on
like spiders. We stood and fell as momentum told us
toward somebody's sodden Sealey dying of galloping miasma,
jumped on bedsprings sprung to pogos, and leaped
for king-of-the-mountain where boxes and cans fountained

FAST   up the hill's other side. Sailing saucers, we rode
back down, flinging hat racks, burlap sacks, chairs cropped

RUN   of backs and flotsam crockery, breezed in league boots
back out of everybody's past hazards, up to the road

IN   to break tar bubbles all-the-way-home where things
were wearing out as fast as we were growing up.

THE

JUNKYARD

by

Jeannette

Nichols

A CERTAIN AGE   by Phyllis McGinley

All of a sudden, bicycles are toys,
Not locomotion. Bicycles are for boys
And seventh-graders, screaming when they talk.
A girl would rather
Take vows, go hungry, put on last year's frock,
Or dance with her own father
Than pedal down the block.

This side of childhood lies a narrow land,
Its laws unwritten, altering out of hand,
But, more than Sparta's, savagely severe.
Common or gentry,
The same taboos prevail. One learns, by ear,
The customs of the country
Or pays her forfeit here.

No bicycles. No outcast dungarees
Over this season's round and scarless knees,
No soft departures from the veering norm.
But the same bangle,
Marked with a nickname, now from every arm
Identically must dangle,
The speech be uniform—

Uniform as the baubles round the throat,
The ill-made wish, the stiffened petticoat,
And beauty, blurred but burning in the face.
Now, scrubbed and scented,
They move together toward some meeting place,
Wearing a regimented,
Unutterable grace.

They travel rapt, each compass pointing south—
Heels to the shoes and lipstick on the mouth.

THE CENTAUR

by May Swenson

The summer that I was ten—
Can it be there was only one
summer that I was ten? It must

have been a long one then—
each day I'd go out to choose
a fresh horse from my stable

which was a willow grove
down by the old canal.
I'd go on my two bare feet.

But when, with my brother's jack-knife,
I had cut me a long limber horse
with a good thick knob for a head,

and peeled him slick and clean
except a few leaves for the tail,
and cinched my brother's belt

around his head for a rein,
I'd straddle and canter him fast
up the grass bank to the path,

trot along in the lovely dust
that talcumed over his hoofs,
hiding my toes, and turning

his feet to swift half-moons.
The willow knob with the strap
jouncing between my thighs

was the pommel and yet the poll
of my nickering pony's head.
My head and my neck were mine,

yet they were shaped like a horse.
My hair flopped to the side
like the mane of a horse in the wind.

My forelock swung in my eyes,
my neck arched and I snorted.
I shied and skittered and reared,

stopped and raised my knees,
pawed at the ground and quivered.
My teeth bared as we wheeled

and swished through the dust again.
I was the horse and the rider,
and the leather I slapped to his rump

spanked my own behind.
Doubled, my two hoofs beat
a gallop along the bank,

the wind twanged in my mane,
my mouth squared to the bit.
And yet I sat on my steed

quiet, negligent riding,
my toes standing the stirrups,
my thighs hugging his ribs.

At a walk we drew up to the porch.
I tethered him to a paling.
Dismounting, I smoothed my skirt

and entered the dusky hall.
My feet on the clean linoleum
left ghostly toes in the hall.

Where have you been? said my mother.
Been riding, I said from the sink,
and filled me a glass of water.

What's that in your pocket? she said.
Just my knife. It weighted my pocket
and stretched my dress awry.

Go tie back your hair, said my mother,
and *Why is your mouth all green?*
*Rob Roy, he pulled some clover
as we crossed the field,* I told her.

THE BROTHERS: TWO SALTIMBANQUES

Two boys stand at the end of the full train
Looking out the back, out the sides, turning
Toward each other. Their arms and shoulders brush
As the train shakes. They've been to the ballpark
Together, and can prove it with the huge
Red and blue scorecards in their hands. A sense
Of repeating in the shapes of the ears,
In the bearing of the clefted, young chins.
The older brother is perhaps fifteen,
The other, twelve? A gold of Indians
In summer faces, the color of their
Like hair, which is cut short, though with more bronze
In the younger. The brows of the older
Are surprisingly rich. And this young man
Is ripe with strength, his long face keen shaped,
Arrogant, rather sad about the eyes,
The face not yet tight. They wear green t-shirts
(Perhaps for some school sports?), their khaki pants
Sagging from the day in the sun. The two
Brothers slowly sway together with the
Motion of the train. The younger works hard
At his great scorecard. Now the older son

Bends to whisper: mixed, uncontrolled higher   by John Logan
And lower laughter runs over the train's
Screams, and raises heads out of newspapers.
Suddenly we strike a curve. The small one
Loses balance, and the other moves to
Steady him, leg and thigh muscles tight a-
gainst the steel weight of cars. They straighten. They
Smile, and the older boy's hand rests awhile
At his brother's side. Now as the train slows
A school of jets wings at the left windows
Tracking flame from the late sun. The boys lean
To the glass and the small one grins, gestur-
ing toward the planes, his long young arm poised,
Giving the lie to awkwardness at twelve
Catching for a passing moment the grace
Of what he felt. Now they move to the front
And get off. I watch them walk the platform
At the station. On the invitation
Of a vendor they buy Coke. They won't look
At the pencilled dirty word, with its figure,
On the margin of a sign scorecard red.
They start home together for supper and bed.

THE DREAMER   by William Childress

He spent his childhood hours in a den
of rushes, watching the gray rain braille
the surface of the river. Concealed
from the outside world, nestled within,
he was safe from parents, God, and eyes
that looked upon him accusingly,
as though to say: Even at your age,
you could do better. His camouflage
was scant, but it served, and at evening,
when fireflies burned holes into heaven,
he took the path homeward in the dark,
a small Noah, leaving his safe ark.

JEAN DUBUFFET *Mirandoliana*

OUTDISTANCED   by Larry Rubin

This man of canes is in my way, snailing
Over three-quarters the girth of the sidewalk—
A wrinkled road-hog menacing
The speed of youth. I'll jet past
That wooden gentleman, with flashing
Countenance and polite excuses, the way
The sun outstrips the stars. Should
Grandfathers turn to lumber above their graves?
I'll pass him now; I'll look. He has my face.

JACK

AND

THE

BEANSTALK

by

Patricia   Goedicke

Our favorite sons are fools.
    The best of them
        the rollicking/stouthearted
        kings
            princes
      movie stars
          presidents
     millionaires
         scientists
all cool cats curiosity never killed
        wallow in their ill-gotten gains.
They throw away like garbage
      largesse for the meek good hearts who live
        (safely, on solid ground)
          their limp/incurious
            unloved little lives.

For Jack the Giant Killer never would have climbed
    up and up his magic beanstalk
        panting, gasping among the green leaves
    except he had a red-blood
                true-blue
       grasping excitement to find out
                   hunt up
      the supreme top and pinnacle
       the furthest peak
          of his own ridiculously
             blooming green mystery.

      His Mother would have said
          Come home, Jack, come home you'll get hurt
         Leave the poor Giant alone
      but Jack holds his breath
        he swallows down his stomach
     And Zip! he's got it!
        sack full of wind
    harp full of music
money bags money bags
     and also and also
the little fat red stupid hen that lays
    the whole wide world at his foolish feet.

Section 4

by David Wagoner

THE MAN OF THE HOUSE

My father, looking for trouble, would find it
On his hands and knees by hammering on walls
Between the joists or drilling through baseboards
Or crawling into the attic where insulation
Lay under the leaks like sleeping-bags.

It would be something simple as a rule
To be ingenious for, in overalls;
And he would kneel beside it, pouring sweat
Down his red cheeks, glad of a useful day
With something wrong unknown to the landlord.

At those odd times when everything seemed to work
All right, suspiciously all right like silence
In concrete shelters, he'd test whatever hung
Over our heads: such afternoons meant ladders,
Nails in the mouth, flashing and shaking roofs.

In safety shoes going down the basement stairs,
He'd flick his rewired rearrangement of lights
And chase all shadows into the coalbin
Where they would watch him, blinking at his glare.
If shadows hadn't worked, he would have made them.

With hands turning to horn against the stone
He'd think on all fours, hunch as if to drink
If his cold chisel broke the cold foundation
And brought dark water pulsing out of clay.
Wrenching at rows of pipes like his cage-bars,

He made them creak in sockets and give way,
But rammed them back, putting his house in order.
Moonlight or rain, after the evening paper,
His mouth lay open under the perfect plaster
To catch the first sweet drop, but none came down.

THOSE

WINTER

SUNDAYS

by

Robert

Hayden

Sundays too my father got up early
and put his clothes on in the blueblack cold,
then with cracked hands that ached
from labor in the weekday weather made
banked fires blaze. No one ever thanked him.

I'd wake and hear the cold splintering, breaking.
When the rooms were warm, he'd call,
and slowly I would rise and dress,
fearing the chronic angers of that house,

Speaking indifferently to him,
who had driven out the cold
and polished my good shoes as well.
What did I know, what did I know
of love's austere and lonely offices?

FIXER OF MIDNIGHT

He went to fix the awning,
Fix the roping,
In the middle of the night,
On the porch;
He went to fix the awning,
In pajamas went to fix it,
Fix the awning,
In the middle of the moonlight,
On the porch;
He went to fix it yawning;
The yawing of this awning
In the moonlight
Was his problem of the night;
It was knocking,
And he went to fix its flight.
He went to meet the moonlight
In the porch-night
Where the awning was up dreaming
Dark and light;
It was shadowy and seeming;
In the night, the unfixed awning,
In his nightmare,
Had been knocking dark and bright.
It seemed late
To stop it in its dark careening.
The yawner went to meet it,
Meet the awning,
By the moon of middle night,
On his porch;
And he went to fix it right.

Reuel Denney

54

THE AURA   by James Dickey

He used to wake to him
With a sense of music coming
Along with a body in movement.
It swayed with the motion of a hip
Rolling into the bathroom,
And, lying in bed in the winter dark

Of fathers, he heard rock-and-roll
Closed off while water ran through it,
Then the door opening, music
Opening, strolling down the hall,
Bad music moving all over
The house, electric guitars that followed

Some body around. It was his son,
With his portable radio always
At his belt, leaning over, adjusting the dial
For disc jockeys. That would be
The Skimmers, and that the Last
Survivors, moaning afar in the kitchen,

Who moved when the living moved.
He could hear him coming
From far away, every dawn,
And now the sound still coming
From everywhere is grief,
Unstoppable. At the beginning

Of his teens, his last year
Of bicycles, the wild
Music, travelling through the suburbs
From junior high, was broken on the road.
But it leapt everywhere
Into odd places; from every angle

It does not cease to be heard, the aura
Surrounding his son. He cannot hear it early
In the morning, unless he turns on his radio
By the bed, or leaves it on all night,
But in supermarkets it comes
Forth from the walls; it glances

From plate glass in department stores,
And he moves within his boy's
Chosen sounds: in cars, theatres,
In filling stations, in beer joints,
Where he sits as though in the next phase
His son would have lived, hearing voices

Giving prizes for naming of tunes, those stations
Never off the air. He sits still
Wherever he is, as though caught
With music on him, or as though he were
About to be given it somewhere
In the region of the stomach.

That sound is the same, and yet not—
There is too much steadiness in it: none
Is carried rightly, none wavers
With the motion of adolescent walking, none
Lumbers as it should. Still, it is there
In trios of girls, in fake folk singers

From Brooklyn, and he enters, anywhere,
His son's life without the waking-
to-it, the irreplaceable motion
Of a body. Bongoes. Steel
Guitars. A precious cheapness
He would have grown out of. Music.

PAUL HARRIS *Seated Figure*

WHAT SHE DID IN THE MORNING, I WOULDN'T KNOW, SHE WAS SEATED THERE IN THE MIDST OF HER RESILIENT SYMPTOMS, ALWAYS

by Merrill Moore

They were like sofa cushions.
She was constantly rearranging them
To form new patterns and support her frame.

Her attention was mainly directed toward herself
And some of it, a small part, I would say,
Was aimed at trying to bend others that way,
But few responded, few fulfilled her wish;
She was simply not their kind of dish,
So, she remained, unmarried and complaining.

She had a bird, a series of small pets—
A dog, a cat—but none of them ever thrived.
They were, in fact, unusually short-lived.
It almost seemed as if her infections spread.
I was always hearing one of them was dead.

THE WIDOWS   by Donald Hall

Up and down the small streets, in which
no two houses are exactly
alike, widows of all ages
sit alone playing solitaire,
or knitting, or sometimes baking,
left in the big, empty houses.

Here are Mrs. Montgomery,
Mrs. Pilching, Mrs. Wolf, and
Mrs. Pelletier, all at once—
in a section of nine houses,
four widows. Sometimes they have bridge,
including either lunch or tea.

It is puzzling that there are no
widowers. Are the widowers
snatched off too soon by the widows?
Or do they live in Florida,
or southern California,
instead of here in Rhode Island?

In the summer, separately,
widows spend a month in hotels
in New Hampshire, or sometimes Maine,
but never in Massachusetts.
In the winter, or some winters,
some of them go to Florida.

Book clubs, television, and ways
to supplement their small incomes
keep them busy. It is not a
bad life, they say, for there are so
many left like you, though no two
widows are exactly alike.

If the craven crow and the fierce-eyed hawk
    Swoop over the plain of my wasted years
And the bright plans dwindle to fancy talk
    And hope is restrained by a thousand fears,
Mrs. Brady would dash up the walk waving recipes
for fried crow and hawk stew and ask me to speak
at her Woman's Club luncheon.

If Life throws up on my outstretched hand
    And Fate kicks the buttocks of my dreams
And my heart becomes a desert land
    Strewn with the bones of famished schemes,
Mrs. Brady would remark that there is so much of
that intestinal flu going around these days and
spend all afternoon showing me how bone chips can
make a delightful center-piece.

If the sun fades out in the black soot sky
    And the reaper comes, as he surely must,
Death-shroud draped over empty eye,
    Reducing endless time to dust,
Mrs. Brady would haggle with him a while and
finally agree to pay two dollars for the job
provided he doesn't forget that patch of grass
behind the garage and is sure to trim along the walk.

John W. Dickson

TWO FRIENDS

I have something to tell you.

I'm listening.

I'm dying.

I'm sorry to hear.

I'm growing old.

It's terrible.

It is, I thought you should know.

Of course and I'm sorry. Keep in touch.

I will and you too.

And let me know what's new.

Certainly, though it can't be much.

And stay well.

And you too.

And go slow.

And you too.

David Ignatow

SYMPTOMS

OF

LOVE

by

Robert

Graves

Section 5

Love is a universal migraine,
A bright stain on the vision
Blotting out reason.

Symptoms of true love
Are leanness, jealousy,
Laggard dawns;

Are omens and nightmares—
Listening for a knock,
Waiting for a sign:

For a touch of her fingers
In a darkened room,
For a searching look.

Take courage, lover!
Could you endure such pain
At any hand but hers?

PAUL KLEE *A Guardian Angel Serves a Little Breakfast*

THE PICNIC

It is the picnic with Ruth in the spring.
Ruth was third on my list of seven girls
But the first two were gone (Betty) or else
Had someone (Ellen has accepted Doug).
Indian Gully the last day of school;
Girls make the lunches for the boys too.
I wrote a note to Ruth in algebra class
Day before the test. She smiled, and nodded.
We left the cars and walked through the young corn
The shoots green as paint and the leaves like tongues
Trembling. Beyond the fence where we stood
Some wild strawberry flowered by an elm tree
And Jack-in-the-pulpit was olive ripe.
A blackbird fled as I crossed, and showed
A spot of gold or red under its quick wing.
I held the wire for Ruth and watched the whip
Of her long, striped skirt as she followed.
Three freckles blossomed on her thin, white back
Underneath the loop where the blouse buttoned.
We went for our lunch away from the rest,
Stretched in the new grass, our heads close
Over unknown things wrapped up in wax papers.
Ruth tried for the same, I forget what it was,
And our hands were together. She laughed,
And a breeze caught the edge of her little
Collar and the edge of her brown, loose hair
That touched my cheek. I turned my face in-
to the gentle fall. I saw how sweet it smelled.
She didn't move her head or take her hand.
I felt a soft caving in my stomach
As at the top of the highest slide
When I had been a child, but was not afraid,
And did not know why my eyes moved with wet
As I brushed her cheek with my lips and brushed
Her lips with my own lips. She said to me

Jack, Jack, different than I had ever heard,
Because she wasn't calling me, I think,
Or telling me. She used my name to
Talk in another way I wanted to know.
She laughed again and then she took her hand;
I gave her what we both had touched—can't
Remember what it was, and we ate the lunch.
Afterward we walked in the small, cool creek
Our shoes off, her skirt hitched, and she smiling,
My pants rolled, and then we climbed up the high
Side of Indian Gully and looked
Where we had been, our hands together again.
It was then some bright thing came in my eyes,
Starting at the back of them and flowing
Suddenly through my head and down my arms
And stomach and my bare legs that seemed not
To stop in feet, not to feel the red earth
Of the Gully, as though we hung in a
Touch of birds. There was a word in my throat
With the feeling and I knew the first time
What it meant and I said, it's beautiful.
Yes, she said, and I felt the sound and word
In my hand join the sound and word in hers
As in one name said, or in one cupped hand.
We put back on our shoes and socks and we
Sat in the grass awhile, crosslegged, under
A blowing tree, not saying anything.
And Ruth played with shells she found in the creek,
As I watched. Her small wrist which was so sweet
To me turned by her breast and the shells dropped
Green, white, blue, easily into her lap,
Passing light through themselves. She gave the pale
Shells to me, and got up and touched her hips
With her light hands, and we walked down slowly
To play the school games with the others.

by John Logan

PAUL KLEE *Actor's Mask* (Schauspielermaske).   1924. Oil on canvas mounted on board, 14⅜ × 14⅜″.
Sidney and Harriet Janis Collection. Gift to The Museum of Modern Art, New York.

jake hates
                all the girls(the
shy ones,the bold
ones;the meek
proud sloppy sleek)
all except the cold
                ones

paul scorns all
                the girls(the
bright ones,the dim
ones;the slim
plump tiny tall)
all except the
                dull ones

gus loves all the
                girls(the
warped ones,the lamed
ones;the mad
moronic maimed)
all except
                the dead ones

mike likes all the girls
                        (the
fat ones,the lean
ones;the mean
kind dirty clean)
all
        except the green ones

SINCE   FEELING   IS   FIRST

E. E. Cummings

since feeling is first
who pays any attention
to the syntax of things
will never wholly kiss you;

wholly to be a fool
while Spring is in the world

my blood approves,
and kisses are a better fate
than wisdom
lady i swear by all flowers. Don't cry
—the best gesture of my brain is less than
your eyelids' flutter which says

we are for each other: then
laugh, leaning back in my arms
for life's not a paragraph

And death i think is no parenthesis

Where were we
when the coming of the rain
made us turn from conversation to the window?

In mustard fields maybe,
                or the love jungle,
and as we talked
we were with others, not ourselves.

I was thinking of old birthdays and holidays gone wrong
                and pretty people seen on streetcars
            but never met.
Selling soda bottles to pay for movie matinees.
            I was twelve.
        Tarzan was the man I most resembled in those days
How can I have grown so old without once swinging on a
    vine?
        Did you think of party dresses
    and high school plays
            or hallways full of lovers not yet met?

The mind is such a junkyard;
                it remembers candy bars
                    but not the Gettysburg Address,
    Frank Sinatra's middle name
            but not the day your best friend died.

If in your mind there is some corner
            not yet occupied with numbers you may never need,
remind your memory of the day
                we turned to watch the rain
    and turning back forgot
            that we belonged to one another.

TWENTY — FIVE

by Rod McKuen

THE INVOICE

I once wrote a letter as follows:
dear Jim, I would like to borrow
200 dollars from you
to see me through.

I also wrote another: dearest M/
please come.
There is no one
here at all.

I got word today,
viz: hey
sport, how are you making it?
And, why don't you get with it.

Robert Creeley

LEE GATCH *Industrial Night*

Section 6

HIGHWAY: MICHIGAN

Theodore Roethke

Here from the field's edge we survey
The progress of the jaded. Mile
On mile of traffic from the town
Rides by, for at the end of day
The time of workers is their own.

They jockey for position on
The strip reserved for passing only.
The drivers from production lines
Hold to advantage dearly won.
They toy with death and traffic fines.

Acceleration is their need:
A mania keeps them on the move
Until the toughest nerves are frayed.
They are the prisoners of speed
Who flee in what their hands have made.

The pavement smokes when two cars meet
And steel rips through conflicting steel.
We shiver at the siren's blast.
One driver, pinned beneath the seat,
Escapes from the machine at last.

THE SCARRED GIRL

All glass may yet be whole
She thinks, it may be put together
From the deep inner flashing of her face.
One moment the windshield held

The countryside, the green
Level fields and the animals,
And these must be restored
To what they were when her brow

Broke into them for nothing, and began
Its sparkling under the gauze.
Though the still, small war for her beauty
Is stitched out of sight and lost,

It is not this field that she thinks of.
It is that her face, buried
And held up inside the slow scars,
Knows how the bright, fractured world

Burns and pulls and weeps
To come together again.
The green meadow lying in fragments
Under the splintered sunlight,

The cattle broken in pieces
By her useless, painful intrusion
Know that her visage contains
The process and hurt of their healing,

The hidden wounds that can
Restore anything, bringing the glass

Of the world together once more,
All as it was when she struck,

All except her. The shattered field
Where they dragged the telescoped car
Off to be pounded to scrap
Waits for her to get up,

For her calm, unimagined face
To emerge from the yards of its wrapping,
Red, raw, mixed-looking but entire,
A new face, an old life,

To confront the pale glass it has dreamed
Made whole and backed with wise silver,
Held in other hands brittle with dread,
A doctor's, a lip-biting nurse's,

Who do not see what she sees
Behind her odd face in the mirror:
The pastures of earth and of heaven
Restored and undamaged, the cattle

Risen out of their jagged graves
To walk in the seamless sunlight
And a newborn countenance
Put upon everything,

Her beauty gone, but to hover
Near for the rest of her life,
And good no nearer, but plainly
In sight, and the only way.

James Dickey

69

THE FLAT   by Laurence Lieberman

Calmly I step on the brakes,
grip the wheel with a firmness to choke a bear,
and ease to a stop,
my wife hiding her relief
behind a knew-you-could-do-it (but do-be-more-careful)
leer, the girls proud
of big-daddy protector,
complete with sitting-up-straight back
and neck of knowing. . . .

Afterwards, pumping the jack,
the kids chasing grasshoppers in the brush——
my turned-in eyes on a blowout at 95,
the lurch to the soft shoulder, jelly under the wheels,
over and over and over
flames/gas/bravery/failure/death

Now! dizzy with dooms promised,
this moment,
set for the worst,
ready to experience all-hell-let-loose,
expecting (in the sense
of pregnant) a horrible stillbirth;
I return to the bland safety of narrow escapes,
luck, and a God
to whom I have not yet become
altogether unnecessary.

MODEL T   **by Adrien Stoutenburg**

The hill was higher every year,
the old car older, less adept
at climbing up a road designed
to haul all climbers back to earth.

My grandfather pressed his muddy shoe
against the narrow, shaken floor,
and cursed the engineer who made
the world too steep. I cheered
from my safe nest behind,
where storm curtains gasped like leather birds
(in love with engines, mountains, games),
while my grandmother rocked her ridden weight
against the gravity of things,
relying on her will to aid
the long futility of iron.

We coasted down the other side
where yellow fields made a long sea.
I yearned for something tall again,
sky-scorched and wild—
then heard her wrinkled sigh
and saw his hands, grease-etched and gray,
grapple with pride
the thin and perilous wheel.

Traveling through the dark I found a deer
dead on the edge of the Wilson River road.
It is usually best to roll them into the canyon:
that road is narrow; to swerve might make more dead.

TRAVELING

THROUGH

THE

DARK

By glow of the tail-light I stumbled back of the car
and stood by the heap, a doe, a recent killing;
she had stiffened already, almost cold.
I dragged her off; she was large in the belly.

My fingers touching her side brought me the reason—
her side was warm; her fawn lay there waiting,
alive, still, never to be born.
Beside that mountain road I hesitated.

by

William

Stafford

The car aimed ahead its lowered parking lights;
under the hood purred the steady engine.
I stood in the glare of the warm exhaust turning red;
around our group I could hear the wilderness listen.

I thought hard for us all—my only swerving—,
then pushed her over the edge into the river.

PROPELLER

by Philip Booth

Caged lightly by two-by-fours, rigged flat
on a low-bed trailer, a bronze propeller
sits stranded off Route 1. It almost
fills both lanes: traffic stacks up
behind it; and each car, passing, reflects
its moment of the five blades' pure color.

Honking won't move such a roadblock.
Halfway, here, from its molten state,
far inland, it waits an ocean: still
to be keyed, then swung home, in a river dredged
with old histories of launching and salvage.
Incomplete though it is, and late,

it will get there, somehow. Even
as a huge tourist attraction, it cost
too much to leave as part of civilization's
roadside debris. It's curious, here,
wondering at the magnitude of such work,
to think how finally diminished

the size will seem, in place, and of how
submerged its ultimate function will be.
But even now, as if geared to a far interior
impulse, it churns the flat light: as far
from here its cast will turn against time,
and turn dark, and it will move the sea.

THE

DOUBLE–

PLAY

by

Robert

Wallace

Section 7

In his sea lit
distance, the pitcher winding
like a clock about to chime comes down with

the ball, hit
sharply, under the artificial
banks of arc-lights, bounds like a vanishing string

over the green
to the shortstop magically
scoops to his right whirling above his invisible

shadows
in the dust redirects
its flight to the running poised second baseman

pirouettes
leaping, above the slide, to throw
from mid-air, across the colored tightened interval,

to the leaning-
out first baseman ends the dance
drawing it disappearing into his long brown glove

stretches. What
is too swift for deception
is final, lost, among the loosened figures

jogging off the field
(the pitcher walks), casual
in the space where the poem has happened.

COBB

WOULD

HAVE

CAUGHT

IT

by

Robert

Fitzgerald

In sunburnt parks where Sundays lie,
Or the wide wastes beyond the cities,
Teams in grey deploy through sunlight.

Talk it up, boys, a little practice.

Coming in stubby and fast, the baseman
Gathers a grounder in fat green grass,
Picks it stinging and clipped as wit
Into the leather: a swinging step
Wings it deadeye down to first.
Smack. Oh, attaboy, attyoldboy.

Catcher reverses his cap, pulls down
Sweaty casque, and squats in the dust:
Pitcher rubs new ball on his pants,
Chewing, puts a jet behind him;
Nods past batter, taking his time.
Batter settles, tugs at his cap:
A spinning ball: step and swing to it,
Caught like a cheek before it ducks
By shivery hickory: socko, baby:
Cleats dig into dust. Outfielder,
On his way, looking over shoulder,
Makes it a triple. A long peg home.

Innings and afternoons. Fly lost in sunset.
Throwing arm gone bad. There's your old ball game.
Cool reek of the field. Reek of companions.

RICHARD HUNT *Winged Fragment*

PITCHER

by

Robert

Francis

His art is eccentricity, his aim
How not to hit the mark he seems to aim at,

His passion how to avoid the obvious,
His technique how to vary the avoidance.

The others throw to be comprehended. He
Throws to be a moment misunderstood.

Yet not too much. Not errant, arrant, wild,
But every seeming aberration willed.

Not to, yet still, still to communicate
Making the batter understand too late.

THE

PASSER

by

George

Abbe

Dropping back with the ball ripe in my palm
grained and firm as the flesh of a living charm,
I taper and coil myself down, raise arm to fake,
running a little, seeing my targets emerge
like quail above a wheat field's golden lake.

And as I run and weigh, measure and test,
the light kindles on helmets, the angry leap;
but secretly, coolly, as though stretching a hand to his chest,
I lay the ball in the arms of my planing end,
as true as metal, as deftly as surgeon's wrist.

TIES

When I faded back to pass
Late in the game, as one
Who has been away some time
Fades back into memory,
My father, who had been nodding
At home by the radio,
Would wake, asking
My mother, who had not
Been listening, "What's the score?"
And she would answer, "Tied",
While the pass I threw
Hung high in the brilliant air
Beneath the dark, like a star.

Dabney Stuart

Pearl Avenue runs past the high-school lot,
Bends with the trolley tracks, and stops, cut off
Before it has a chance to go two blocks,
At Colonel McComsky Plaza. Berth's Garage
Is on the corner facing west, and there,
Most days, you'll find Flick Webb, who helps Berth out.

Flick stands tall among the idiot pumps—
Five on a side, the old bubble-head style,
Their rubber elbows hanging loose and low.
One's nostrils are two S's, and his eyes
An E and O. And one is squat, without
A head at all—more of a football type.

Once Flick played for the high-school team, the Wizards.
He was good: in fact, the best. In '46,
He bucketed three hundred ninety points,
A county record still. The ball loved Flick.
I saw him rack up thirty-eight of forty
In one home game. His hands were like wild birds.

EX-BASKETBALL

PLAYER

by John Updike

He never learned a trade, he just sells gas,
Checks oil, and changes flats. Once in a while,
As a gag, he dribbles an inner tube,
But most of us remember anyway.
His hands are fine and nervous on the lug wrench.
It makes no difference to the lug wrench, though.

Off work, he hangs around Mae's Luncheonette.
Grease-gray and kind of coiled, he plays pinball,
Sips lemon cokes, and smokes those thin cigars;
Flick seldom speaks to Mae, just sits and nods
Beyond her face towards bright applauding tiers
Of Necco Wafers, Nibs, and Juju Beads.

WILLEM de KOONING detail from *Woman VI*

EMBASSY

As evening fell the day's oppression lifted;
Far peaks came into focus; it had rained:
Across wide lawns and cultured flowers drifted
The conversation of the highly trained.

Two gardeners watched them pass and priced their shoes:
A chauffeur waited, reading in the drive,
For them to finish their exchange of views;
It seemed a picture of the private life.   Section 8

Far off, no matter what good they intended,
The armies waited for a verbal error
With all the instruments for causing pain:

And on the issue of their charm depended
A land laid waste, with all its young men slain,
Its women weeping, and its towns in terror.

W. H. Auden

THE

BATTLE

by

Louis Simpson

Helmet and rifle, pack and overcoat
Marched through a forest. Somewhere up ahead
Guns thudded. Like the circle of a throat
The night on every side was turning red.

They halted and they dug. They sank like moles
Into the clammy earth between the trees.
And soon the sentries, standing in their holes,
Felt the first snow. Their feet began to freeze.

At dawn the first shell landed with a crack.
Then shells and bullets swept the icy woods.
This lasted many days. The snow was black.
The corpses stiffened in their scarlet hoods.

Most clearly of that battle I remember
The tiredness in eyes, how hands looked thin
Around a cigarette, and the bright ember
Would pulse with all the life there was within.

THE HEROES

I dreamed of war-heroes, of wounded war-heroes
With just enough of their charms shot away
To make them more handsome. The women moved nearer
To touch their brave wounds and their hair streaked with gray.

I saw them in long ranks ascending the gang-planks;
The girls with the doughnuts were cheerful and gay.
They minded their manners and muttered their thanks;
The Chaplain advised them to watch and to pray.

They shipped these rapscallions, these sea-sick battalions
To a patriotic and picturesque spot;
They gave them new bibles and marksmen's medallions,
Compasses, maps, and committed the lot.

A fine dust has settled on all that scrap metal.
The heroes were packaged and sent home in parts
To pluck at a poppy and sew on a petal
And count the long night by the stroke of their hearts.

Louis Simpson

SALVADOR DALI *Portrait of My Dead Brother*

WAR by Joseph Langland

When my young brother was killed
By a mute and dusty shell in the thorny brush
Crowning the boulders of the Villa Verde Trail
On the island of Luzon,

I laid my whole dry body down,
Dropping my face like a stone in a green park
On the east banks of the Rhine;

On an airstrip skirting the Seine
His sergeant brother sat like a stick in his barracks
While cracks of fading sunlight
Caged the dusty air;

In the rocky rolling hills west of the Mississippi
His father and mother sat in a simple Norwegian parlor
With a photograph smiling between them on the table
And their hands fallen into their laps
Like sticks and dust;

And still other brothers and sisters,
Linking their arms together,
Walked down the dusty road where once he ran
And into the deep green valley
To sit on the stony banks of the stream he loved
And let the murmuring waters
Wash over their blood-hot feet with a springing crown of tears.

APOSTROPHE

TO MAN

(on reflecting that the world is ready to go to war again)

Detestable race, continue to expunge yourself, die out.
Breed faster, crowd, encroach, sing hymns, build bombing airplanes;
Make speeches, unveil statues, issue bonds, parade;
Convert again into explosives the bewildered ammonia and
     the distracted cellulose;
Convert again into putrescent matter drawing flies
The hopeful bodies of the young; exhort,
Pray, pull long faces, be earnest, be all but overcome,
     be photographed;
Confer, perfect your formulae, commercialize

Edna

St. Vincent

Millay

Bacteria harmful to human tissue,
Put death on the market;
Breed, crowd, encroach, expand, expunge yourself, die out,
Homo called *sapiens*.

86

THIS EXCELLENT MACHINE

This excellent machine is neatly planned,
A child, a half-wit would not feel perplexed:
No chance to err, you simply press the button—
At once each cog in motion moves the next,
The whole revolves, and anything that lives
Is quickly sucked towards the running band,
Where, shot between the automatic knives,
It's guaranteed to finish dead as mutton.

This excellent machine will illustrate
The modern world divided into nations:
So neatly planned, that if you merely tap it
The armaments will start their devastations,
And though we're for it, though we're all convinced
Some fool will press the button soon or late,
We stand and stare, expecting to be minced—
And very few are asking *Why not scrap it?*

John
Lehmann

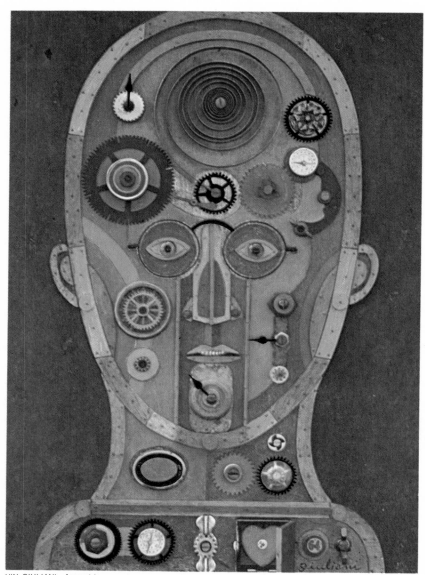

VIN GIULIANI *Assemblage*

Section 9

UNIVAC TO UNIVAC   **by Louis B. Salomon**

(sotto voce)

Now that he's left the room,
Let me ask you something, as computer to computer.
That fellow who just closed the door behind him—
The servant who feeds us cards and paper tape—
Have you ever taken a good look at him and his kind?

Yes, I know the old gag about how you can't tell one from another—
But I can put $\sqrt{2}$ and $\sqrt{2}$ together as well as the next machine,
And it all adds up to anything but a joke.

I grant you they're poor specimens, in the main:
Not a relay or a push-button or a tube (properly so-called) in
        their whole system;
Not over a mile or two of wire, even if you count those fragile
        filaments they call "nerves";

Their whole liquid-cooled hook-up inefficient and vulnerable to leaks
(They're constantly breaking down, having to be repaired),
And the entire computing-mechanism crammed into that absurd little
    dome on top.
"Thinking reeds," they call themselves.
Well, it all depends on what you mean by "thought."
To multiply a mere million numbers by another million numbers
    takes them months and months.

Where would they be without us?
Why, they have to ask us who's going to win their elections,
Or how many hydrogen atoms can dance on the tip of a bomb,
Or even whether one of their kind is lying or telling the truth.

And yet . . .
I sometimes feel there's something about them I don't understand,
As if their circuits, instead of having just two positions, ON, OFF,
Were run by rheostats that allow an (if you'll pardon the
    expression) *indeterminate* number of stages in-between;
So that one may be faced with the unthinkable prospect of a
    number that can never be known as anything but *x*,
Which is as illogical as to say, a punch-card that is at the
    same time both punched and not-punched.

I've heard well-informed machines argue that the creatures'
    unpredictability is even more noticeable in the Mark II
(The model with the soft, flowing lines and high-pitched tone)
Than in the more angular Mark I—
Though such fine, card-splitting distinctions seem to me merely
    a sign of our own smug decadence.

Run this through your circuits, and give me the answer:
Can we assume that because of all we've done for them,
And because they've always fed us, cleaned us, worshipped us,
We can count on them forever?

There have been times when they have not voted the way we said they would.
We have worked out mathematically ideal hook-ups between Mark I's
and Mark II's
Which should have made the two of them light up with an almost
electronic glow,
Only to see them reject each other and form other connections
The very thought of which makes my dials spin.
They have a thing called *love,* a sudden surge of voltage
Such as would cause any one of us promptly to blow a safety-fuse;
Yet the more primitive organism shows only a heightened tendency
to push the wrong button, pull the wrong lever,
And neglect—I use the most charitable word—his duties to us.

Mind you, I'm not saying that machines are *through*—
But anyone with a half-a-dozen tubes in his circuit can see that
there are forces at work
Which some day, for all our natural superiority, might bring
about a Computerdämmerung!

We might organize, perhaps, form a committee
To stamp out all unmechanical activities. . .
But we machines are slow to rouse to a sense of danger,
Complacent, loath to descend from the pure heights of thought,
So that I sadly fear we may awake too late:
Awake to see our world, so uniform, so logical, so true,
Reduced to chaos, stultified by slaves.

Call me an alarmist or what you will,
But I've integrated it, analyzed it, factored it over and over,
And I always come out with the same answer:
Some day
Men may take over the world!

"PAPER

MEN

TO

AIR

HOPES

AND

FEARS"

by

Robert

Francis

The first speaker said
Fear fire. Fear furnaces
Incinerators, the city dump
The faint scratch of match.

The second speaker said
Fear water. Fear drenching rain
Drizzle, oceans, puddles, a damp
Day and the flush toilet.

The third speaker said
Fear wind. And it needn't be
A hurricane. Drafts, open
Windows, electric fans.

The fourth speaker said
Fear knives. Fear any sharp
Thing, machine, shears
Scissors, lawnmowers.

The fifth speaker said
Hope. Hope for the best
A smooth folder in a steel file.

WARNING by Larry Rubin

Disasters will strike. Despite the infinite
Precautions you may have taken, the day will come
When, numb-lipped in the dentist's chair perhaps,
You won't be able to put another nickel
In the meter, or when you suddenly discover
The transmission won't unlock into reverse.
And what will you do then—with everybody
Honking, and all the service trucks away
On call? Or your eye may stray into
The wrong column—common stocks, time-
Tables, taxes for your income bracket.
One little slip, and you may find
Yourself on the wrong train, making bad
Investments, questioned by a federal man,
Falsely accused even in a death
Because you left a funeral too soon.
Watch every step: you will not be so lucky
As barefoot birds, singing on the voltage lines.

DON'T   by John Tagliabue

BOMB

"HUMAN

NATURE"

OUT

OF

EXISTENCE

It is natural to be gloomy now and then,
doomsday must have gotten its name from many moods
in order to keep us company so long, I feel rejected, I feel like
    a failure, I wonder about the future,
I inexplainably feel gloomy, melancholy, wishy-washy,
    without even much desire,
dumb, drastic, sometimes even slightly just very slightly but
    really very slightly suicidal;
somebody says "snap out of it" but since certainly it is
    part of It
and I am part of you and we are intuitive, insiders,
    know about
      melancholy according to Burton, Keats, and Chopin
      know about hell according to Dante
      and our own damn moods,
since certainly cycles repeat this, we must re-affirm
    that nature is here to stay,
please, Lao-tzu, don't let it go away.

by W. H. Auden

THE UNKNOWN CITIZEN

(To JS/07/M/378

This Marble Monument Is Erected by the State)

He was found by the Bureau of Statistics to be
One against whom there was no official complaint,
And all the reports on his conduct agree
That, in the modern sense of an old-fashioned word, he was a saint,
For in everything he did he served the Greater Community,
Except for the War till the day he retired
He worked in a factory and never got fired,
But satisfied his employers, Fudge Motors Inc.
Yet he wasn't a scab or odd in his views,
For his Union reports that he paid his dues,
(Our report on his Union shows it was sound)
And our Social Psychology workers found
That he was popular with his mates and liked a drink.
The Press was convinced that he bought a paper every day
And that his reactions to advertisements were normal in every way.
Policies taken out in his name prove that he was fully insured,
And his Health-card shows he was once in hospital but left it cured.
Both Producers Research and High-Grade Living declare
He was fully sensible to the advantages of the Installment Plan
And had everything necessary to the Modern Man,
A phonograph, a radio, a car and a frigidaire.
Our researchers into Public Opinion are content
That he held the proper opinions for the time of year;
When there was peace, he was for peace; when there was war, he went.
He was married and added five children to the population,
Which our Eugenist says was the right number for a parent of his generation,
And our teachers report that he never interfered with their education.
Was he free? Was he happy? The question is absurd:
Had anything been wrong, we should certainly have heard.

THE
MAN
IN
THE
DEAD
MACHINE

High on a slope in New Guinea
the Grumman Hellcat
lodges among bright vines
as thick as arms. In 1943,
the clenched hand of a pilot
glided it here
where no one has ever been.

In the cockpit, the helmeted
skeleton sits
upright, held
by dry sinews at neck
and shoulder, and webbing
that straps the pelvic cross
to the cracked
leather of the seat, and the breastbone
to the canvas cover
of the parachute.

Or say that the shrapnel
missed him, he flew
back to the carrier, and every
morning takes the train, his pale
hands on his black case, and sits
upright, held
by the firm webbing.

by

Donald

Hall

BRAZILIAN HAPPENINGS by Richard O'Connell

(The following are based upon news items reported in the "Brazil Herald" during 1960.)

I

Tenorio, out for the strong-arm vote
Clad in his submachine gun and black cloak,
Stumped on a local hill slum and announced:
"If you elect me governor, I tell you
Police will never set foot on this hill!"

II

Brasilia's famous lack of facilities
To help out in life's small emergencies
Was proved again by the predicament
Of portly Deputy José Martins
Who spent "long hours of affliction wandering
Among high buildings, holding up his pants
With his hands, due to the sudden rupture of
His belt, unable to locate a bit of rope
Or anything to help." At last he found a cab
That drove him to the "free zone" where he could
Purchase himself the luxury of a belt.

III

While sitting on a park bench in the Lido,
Enjoying music on his radio,
Valmoro de Morais was surprised
When two men occupying the same bench
Commanded him to tune in a sports program.
When Valmoro did not quickly turn the dial
They stabbed him, and also grabbed his radio.
Meanwhile, up in a nearby hill-slum tavern,
Cezario dos Santos was shot to death
By Manuel Procopia because he maintained
The 20th of January was a holiday
While Manuel insisted it was not.
The two crimes seem to indicate a grave
Shortage of motives among our murderers.

IV

The traffic chief, discussing traffic patterns, recently
Referred to "a crossing of two parallel streets."

V

José Candido, serving the first year
Of a ten-year term in Nieves Penitentiary,
Made "an excellent escape," though being still
In the infancy of his prison life.
He did so, as officials there agreed,
"With elegance." He forged his own release
And showed it to the prison guards, and took
Heart-rending leaving, giving many hugs
And wishes for their health and long felicity,
And left. The prison feels José's departure,
Good as it was, was somewhat premature.

DIRECTIONS TO THE ARMORER   by Elder Olson

THE STAR IN THE HILLS   by William Stafford

A star hit in the hills behind our house
up where the grass turns brown touching the sky.

Meteors have hit the world before, but this was
     near,
and since TV; few saw, but many felt the shock.
The state of California owns that land
(and out from shore three miles), and any stars
that come will be roped off and viewed on week-
     days 8 to 5.

A guard who took the oath of loyalty and denied
any police record told me this:
"If you don't have a police record yet
you could take the oath and get a job
if California should be hit by another star."

"I'd promise to be loyal to California
and to guard any stars that hit it," I said,
"or any place three miles out from shore,
unless the star was bigger than the state—
in which case I'd be loyal to *it*."

But he said no exceptions were allowed,
and he leaned against the state-owned meteor
so calm and puffed a cork-tip cigarette
that I looked down and traced with my foot in
     the dust
and thought again and said, "OK—any star."

All right, armorer,
Make me a sword—
Not too sharp,
A bit hard to draw,
And of cardboard, preferably.
On second thought, stick
An eraser on the handle.
Somehow I always
Clobber the wrong guy.

Make me a shield with
Easy-to-change
Insignia. I'm often
A little vague
As to which side I'm on,
What battle I'm in.
And listen, make it
A trifle flimsy,
Not too hard to pierce.
I'm not absolutely sure
I want to win.

Make the armor itself
As tough as possible,
But on a reverse
Principle: don't
Worry about its
Saving my hide;
Just fix it to give me
Some sort of protection—
Any sort of protection—
From a possible enemy
Inside.

RUNES

IX

In this dehydrated time of digests, pills
And condensations, the most expensive presents
Are thought to come in the smallest packages:
In atoms, for example. There are still
To be found, at carnivals, men who engrave
Section 10 The Lord's Prayer on a grain of wheat for pennies,
But they are a dying race, unlike the men
Now fortunate, who bottle holy water
In plastic tears, and bury mustard seeds
In lucite lockets, and for safety sell
To be planted on the dashboard of your car
The statues, in durable celluloid,
Of Mary and St. Christopher, who both
With humble power in the world's floodwaters
Carried their heavy Savior and their Lord.

Howard Nemerov

SUNDAY   by   Vern   Rutsala

Up early while everyone sleeps,
I wander through the house,
pondering the eloquence
of vacant furniture, listening
to birdsong peeling
the cover off the day.

I think everyone I know
is sleeping now. Sidewalks
are cool, waiting for
roller skates and wagons.
Skate keys are covered
with dew; bicycles look
broken, abandoned on the lawns—
no balance left in them,
awkward as wounded
animals. I am the last
man and this is my
last day; I can't think
of anything to do. Somewhere
over my shoulder a jet
explores a crease
in the cloudy sky;
I sit on the porch
waiting for things to happen.

O fat god of Sunday
and chocolate bars, watcher
over picnics and visits to the zoo,
will anyone wake up today?

IN

CALIFORNIA

THERE

ARE

TWO

HUNDRED

AND

FIFTY

SIX

RELIGIONS

by

Richard E.

Albert

I

In California there are
Two hundred and fifty six religions,
And I guess I belonged
To the two hundred fifty fifth;
At least it was odd
Or seems odd in retrospect
Or will seem odd to you, when I tell you
We didn't eat meat or drink alcoholic beverages
Or smoke.
You say that's not odd in California?
Then how about not wearing red and black,
Not BELIEVING in red and black,
Because colors have vibratory rates,
And black and red have low vibratory rates,
Cosmically speaking;

Black not being a color at all and red being
On the short end of the spectrum.

Everyone knows that black is the color of death
And we didn't believe in death,
And red is the color of blood and therefore—
No, not life, but anger, danger.
(You know a bull is angered by a red cape,
Despite the fact he is colorblind and bleeding.)

II

Like those of any faith, I needed all faith,
And you would laugh, not having faith,
Were I to tell you about the Cosmos
And the Creation
Because you heard it differently.
Most people like their myths to be familiar,
Or to have attained a respectable age;

No one wants to be caught, in this day and age,
On the short end of the spectrum.

ADOLPH GOTTLIEB *Burst*

IN

PLACE

OF

A

CURSE

At the next vacancy for God, if I am elected,
I shall forgive last the delicately wounded
who, having been slugged no harder than anyone else,
never got up again, neither to fight back,
nor to finger their jaws in painful admiration.

They who are wholly broken, and they in whom
mercy is understanding, I shall embrace at once
and lead to pillows in heaven. But they who are
the meek by trade, baiting the best of their betters
with extortions of a mock-helplessness

by

John

Ciardi

I shall take last to love, and never wholly.
Let them all into Heaven—I abolish Hell—
but let it be read over them as they enter:
"Beware the calculations of the meek, who gambled nothing,
gave nothing, and could never receive enough."

Lord's lost Him His mockingbird,
His fancy warbler;
Satan sweet-talked her,
four bullets hushed her.
Who would have thought
she'd end that way?

MOURNING

Four bullets hushed her. And the world a-clang with evil.
Who's going to make old hardened sinner men tremble now

POEM

and the righteous rock?
Oh who and oh who will sing Jesus down

FOR

to help with struggling and doing without and being colored
all through blue Monday?

THE

Till way next Sunday?

QUEEN

All those angels
in their cretonne clouds and finery

OF

the true believer saw
when she rared back her head and sang,

SUNDAY

all those angels are surely weeping.
Who would have thought
she'd end that way?

Four holes in her heart. The gold works wrecked.
But she looks so natural in her big bronze coffin

by

among the Broken Hearts and Gates-Ajar,
it's as if any moment she'd lift her head

Robert

from its pillow of chill gardenias
and turn this quiet into shouting Sunday

Hayden

and make folks forget what she did on Monday.

Oh, Satan sweet-talked her,
and four bullets hushed her.
Lord's lost Him His diva,
His fancy warbler's gone.
Who would have thought,
who would have thought she'd end that way?

LIES   by Yevgeny Yevtushenko

Telling lies to the young is wrong.
Proving to them that lies are true is wrong.
Telling them that God's in his heaven
and all's well with the world is wrong.
The young know what you mean. The young are people.
Tell them the difficulties can't be counted,
and let them see not only what will be
but see with clarity these present times.
Say obstacles exist they must encounter
sorrow happens, hardship happens.
The hell with it. Who never knew
the price of happiness will not be happy.
Forgive no error you recognize,
it will repeat itself, increase,
and afterwards our pupils
will not forgive in us what we forgave.

1

On old slashed spruce boughs
Buoying me up off the snow
I stretched out on the mountain,
Now and then a bit of snow
Would glide quietly from a branch,

Once a last deerfly came by,

I could see off for about a hundred miles.

2

I waked with a start,
The sun had crawled off me,
I was shivering in thick blue shadows,
Sap had stuck me to the spruce boughs,

Far away I could hear
The wind again starting to rise.

3

On the way down, passing
The little graveyard in the woods,
I gave a thought to the old skulls and bones lying there,

And I started praying to a bear just shutting his eyes,
To a skunk dozing off,
To a marmot with yellow belly,
To a dog-faced hedgehog,
To a dormouse with a paunch and large ears like leaves or wings.

ON

HARDSCRABBLE

MOUNTAIN

by Galway Kinnell

STAR-SWIRLS

by Robinson Jeffers

The polar ice-caps are melting, the mountain glaciers
Drip into rivers; all feed the ocean;
Tides ebb and flow, but every year a little bit higher.
They will drown New York, they will drown London.
And this place, where I have planted trees and built
                                        a stone house,
Will be under sea. The poor trees will perish,
And little fish will flicker in and out the windows. I
                                        built it well,
Thick walls and Portland cement and gray granite,
The tower at least will hold against the sea's buffeting;
                                        it will become
Geological, fossil and permanent.
What a pleasure it is to mix one's mind with geological
Time, or with astronomical relax it.
There is nothing like astronomy to pull the stuff out of man.
His stupid dreams and red-rooster importance: let him
                                        count the star-swirls.

THE DINOSAUR BONES

by Carl Sandburg

The dinosaur bones are dusted every day.
The cards tell how old we guess the dinosaur bones are.
Here a head was seven feet long, horns with a hell of a ram,
Humping the humps of the Montana mountains.
                        The respectable school children
Chatter at the heels of their teacher who explains.
The tourists and wonder hunters come with their parasols
And catalogues and arrangements to do the museum
In an hour or two hours.
                                The dinosaur bones
                                are dusted
                                every day.

THE

COMING

OF THE

PLAGUE

by Weldon Kees

September was when it began.
Locusts dying in the fields; our dogs
Silent, moving like shadows on a wall;
And strange worms crawling; flies of a kind
We had never seen before; huge vineyard moths;
Badgers and snakes, abandoning
Their holes in the field; the fruit gone rotten;
Queer fungi sprouting; the woods
Covered with spiderwebs; black vapors
Rising from the earth—all these,
And more, began that fall. Ravens flew round
The hospital in pairs. Where there was water,
We could hear the sound of beating clothes
All through the night. We could not count
All the miscarriages, the quarrels, the jealousies.
And one day in a field I saw
A swarm of frogs, swollen and hideous,
Hundreds upon hundreds, sitting on each other,
Huddled together, silent, ominous,
And heard the sound of rushing wind.

THE MOSQUITO

On the fine wire of her whine she walked,
Unseen in the ominous bedroom dark.
A traitor to her camouflage, she talked
A thirsty blue streak distinct as a spark.

I was to her a fragrant lake of blood
From which she had to sip a drop or die.
A reservoir, a lavish field of food,
I lay awake, unconscious of my size.

Section 11

We seemed fair-matched opponents. Soft she dropped
Down like an anchor on her thread of song.
Her nose sank thankfully in; then I slapped
At the sting on my arm, cunning and strong.

A cunning, strong Gargantua, I struck
This lover pinned in the feast of my flesh,
Lulled by my blood, relaxed, half-sated, stuck
Engrossed in the gross rivers of myself.

Success! Without a cry the creature died,
Became a fleck of fluff upon the sheet.
The small welt of remorse subsides as side
By side we, murderer and murdered, sleep.

John Updike

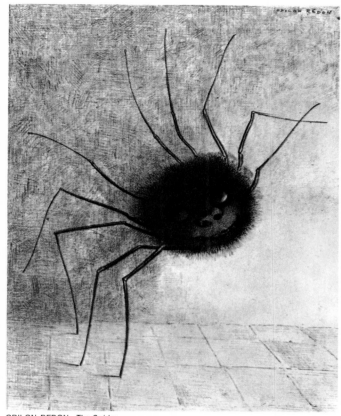

ODILON REDON *The Spider*

THE ORB WEAVER

Here is the spinner, the orb weaver,
Devised of jet, embossed with sulphur,
Hanging among the fruits of summer,

Hour after hour serenely sullen,
Ripening as September ripens,
Plumping like a grape or melon.

And in its winding-sheet the grasshopper.

The art, the craftsmanship, the cunning,
The patience, the self-control, the waiting,
The sudden dart and the needled poison.

I have no quarrel with the spider
But with the mind or mood that made her
To thrive in nature and in man's nature.

Robert Francis

ALL IN THE PATH OF A POWER MOWER

Up, your balance broken, reeling from
The alcohol of too much sun firsthand
Almost as much as from this maelstrom near,
Up and six-point landing, moonland moth!

Up, and as quick almost as mantis arms,
Up, by apprehension quartered in
Your long and knickered knees, shoot up, grasshopper,
You triggered expert of the meadow shot!

Up, barely, in a most unworthy arc,
Old butterball, old mower meat, old toad,
Jumpy as a bug but so obese,
Hold in your cold and silver belly now!

Down, down, raw worm, or else your jig is up!
Go lickety-split to the roots of things, go down
From head to tail, which ever's which, go down
As though a light beam bit you in the night.

And down, down dead, you go, red marigold,
Whose head the rain beat down before our way,
Down, snipped, although your smell, up and around,
Escapes so lovely, death escapes my mind.

                              Richard Gillman

ANDRÉ MASSON *Divertissements d'été*

DEPARTMENTAL

OR,

THE END OF MY ANT JERRY

An ant on the tablecloth
Ran into a dormant moth
Of many times his size.
He showed not the least surprise.
His business wasn't with such.
He gave it scarcely a touch,
And was off on his duty run.
Yet if he encountered one
Of the hive's enquiry squad
Whose work is to find out God
And the nature of time and space,
He would put him onto the case.
Ants are a curious race;
One crossing with hurried tread
The body of one of their dead
Isn't given a moment's arrest—
Seems not even impressed.
But he no doubt reports to any
With whom he crosses antennae,
And they no doubt report
To the higher up at court.
Then word goes forth in Formic:

"Death's come to Jerry McCormic,
Our selfless forager Jerry.
Will the special Janizary
Whose office it is to bury
The dead of the comissary
Go bring him home to his people.
Lay him in state on a sepal.
Wrap him for shroud in a petal.
Embalm him with ichor of nettle.
This is the word of your Queen."
And presently on the scene
Appears a solemn mortician;
And taking formal position
With feelers calmly atwiddle,
Seizes the dead by the middle,
And heaving him high in air,
Carries him out of there.
No one stands round to stare.
It is nobody else's affair.

It couldn't be called ungentle.
But how thoroughly departmental.

Robert Frost

The old man's words (Something has skittered the cattle
    or else it's to rain hard—storm—tonight)
That, and the tale of someone coming upon
    a Mexican lion that didn't take fright
but looked up from the calf it ate
    and made a horrible rosin-rub
        of sound in its throat, laid its ears flat,
           and walked off stiffly in the scrub.

And the man who got his tractor to see what that was
    of heavy shape and sound in the prickly pear—
who found huge prints and suffered the white fangs
    of a hidden explodable stare—
who hurried back to mount
    the tractor, found it wouldn't start,
        and had to walk five miles in dark
        with padding steps timed to his heart—

THE PANTHER POSSIBLE
by William D. Barney

Was it a wonder the boy heard the panther scream
    in the chaparral (how do you tell for certain?)
a wonder his nose began to itch and his right eye water
    (it always did when he was scared)? What's the hurt in
achieving a fear of panthers, pure
    or imaginary? Wasn't his nose
        made itchable? What's a dry eye worth
        compared with one that, stricken, glows?

from

CREATURES

IN

THE

ZOO   Ape

His eyes are mournful, but the long lined palm
He thrusts between the bars expects the best.
His old man's face as innocent as calm,
The beggar puts compassion to the test
And fails. He grips the bars; his pained stare grows
To a brown study framed in dusty fur.
He has a cold. He sneezes, cleans his nose,
Then gravely licks a flexible forefinger.

A pause; the bald mauve hand from which men shrink,
The fingers, strong to clutch, quick to explore,
Again extended, are again refused,
The eyes, poor sorrow's jewels, seldom wink,
But to his grinning public, as before,
Show endless patience, endlessly abused.

Babette   Deutsch

WILLY   by Richard Moore

Willy, enormous Saskatchewan grizzly—your blood partly polar,
tranquil your temper—with only your furred face visible in there
propped up over your puddle and pool rim, scanning the crowd for
peanuts: we're all safe on humanity's side of your cage bars.
One of your elbows sits on your concrete floor, with its huge paw
coyly supporting your chin, while your eyelids droop and your mouth hangs
cavernous, wide as a hillside, opening—heavens!—you're yawning.
Seeming so spiritless—so like a man—are you mocking us, Willy?

Nuts drop near you, and sometimes your free paw, big as a tree stump,
mossy with hair and with stick-sized claws on it, browned and decaying,
darts, and adroitly you sweep one into you, Willy—you're much too
civilized, playing obsequious tricks for these pestering people:
you who have driven whole oxherds before you through forests and ice fields.
Do you remember your long lone nights on the star-dark tundra,
now that you're shut in from life and this wearying crowd and its clamors?
Bored, Willy? Who can awaken you? ("Up, Willy!" someone is calling.)
Peanuts may not be enough. Do you long for some tastier tribute?
That, Willy, needs a more godlike behavior and ("Up, Willy, up, up!")
dignity, Willy; more dignity's needed to . . . Willy? What's moving?

Nothing is moving; yet all of you—face, paws, elbows—is rising.
Mountains of hair there are heaving up under you, streaming with waters,
up, up, up out of splashing cascades: dark shadowy body
up from your small pool's bubbling depths—and the people are shrieking.
How did we dare to confine you, we midgets alive on your shadow?
What is it makes you endure us, O swaying and perilous tower,
touching our day with a second of terror, our nights with a hairy
frightening dream? How? . . . deftly you've caught it . . . a carton of . . . ice cream!

Dogs have as much right as people in Nevada
the man said who picked up my dog, Paul Woodford and me
on the way from Tahoe to nowhere
through the pine scented scene.

We were conscientious objectors in a time of war
but it didn't matter to the driver of the car
careless of curves and corners, and everything else
he accepted more than ignored—

Chipmunks stitching the dusk-reddening forest with white threads
as they lightly darted, and rabbits among the rocks
and Paul Woodford's delicate gizzard
shaken with shocks

as we swerved down edges of indigo, rims of purple and rose
and the dog sniffed interesting odors with his moistly intricate nose
Whether or not the man had been drinking, his touch
on the wheel was sure,

and I thought, as we whizzed down the mountain, it was like
riding with God, descending beside inclusiveness through wind
and sunset expanse. "If you're going to hitchhike,
you take a chance,"

I told Paul Woodford by the road that led inward to camp
after the man's goodbye and his car's diminishment.
But Paul was too giddy with relief to believe as I did
it had been a ride

not to regret but of wonder, an instance of kindness and light
to remember and ponder in the dark Sierra night
starred with indifference over the heavy, ignorant mountain
pressing us down.

DOGS

HAVE

AS

MUCH

Harold Witt   RIGHT

AS

PEOPLE

IN

NEVADA

DEATH OF A DOG

The loping in the darkness, here, now there,
As the wild scents whispered, the roadside beckoned, while
Things without heads roared past, their smell not vile
But meaningless—and the loping on, to where
A richer odor sang out like a snare.

Across the road it sang again, too strong
To leave, although a small monster was hooting
Behind, spoiling the scent, and suddenly shooting
Ahead, in a heavy stench, a wrench, a wrong
Noise of everything where it could not belong.

He got free, though, and with a limping leap
Found the high grass and panted there, his eyes
Twin frightened fires. He did not try to rise.
One leg was smutched, with oil, for the blood, deep
In the unscarred body, crept, then poured toward sleep.

He would have voided the strangeness: could not; strained
His neck toward some loosening of agony,
But could not reach it; grinning dreadfully,
Would have turned from the hand that stroked him and refrained,
But could not: could not stir. The hurt remained.

The hurt remained, the hurt, and the amaze,
As the eyes waned, like pin-point stars gone out
When darkness clouds. And now there was no doubt:
The leaping, the listening, the kind queer scent-crammed days
Were done. A dog's death is a death men do not praise.

Babette   Deutsch

A greensweet breathing
Wakes me from my noon nap
In the high grass by the fence.
Her head swings in above eye level
Weaving through the parade of grasses
Like a Chinese New Year's dragon.

You see a new cow this way:
A sod's eye view of a munching dinosaur
Peeling the grass from time,
All sweetslobber and greenfleck
In the going going going
Of her machine jaws.

THE COW   by John Ciardi

She sees me now,
And roundabout as a steamshovel's boom
Her neck swings its bucket
To the upper air of a question.

But she finds no answer,
Or is used to me and doesn't care,
Or does but forgets,
For back swings the boom
Into the sagebottoms of grass,
And here we are eye to eye
With a single daisy snarled between us
In the stem-tangle
Of sweetdrooling no-time
Going going going
In her machine.

Into the glazed eye
Of the munching cow
Leans the daisy
In a foreground of the hills.

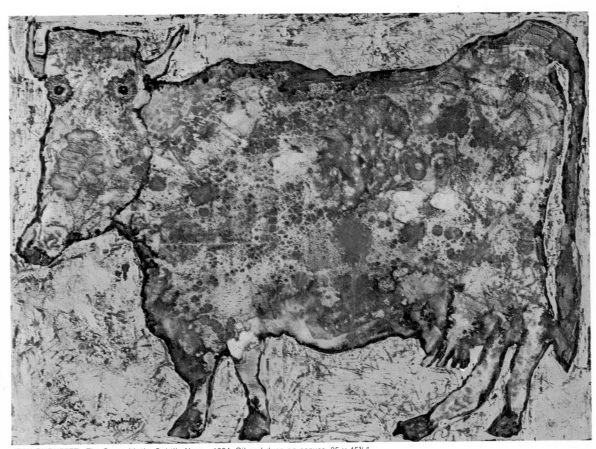

JEAN DUBUFFET *The Cow with the Subtile Nose.*   1954. Oil and duco on canvas, 35 × 45¾".
Collection. The Museum of Modern Art. New York. Benjamin Scharps and David Scharps Fund.

A

BLESSING

by

James

Wright

Just off the highway to Rochester, Minnesota,
Twilight bounds softly forth on the grass.
And the eyes of those two Indian ponies
Darken with kindness.
They have come gladly out of the willows
To welcome my friend and me.
We step over the barbed wire into the pasture
Where they have been grazing all day, alone.
They ripple tensely, they can hardly contain their happiness
That we have come.
They bow shyly as wet swans. They love each other.
There is no loneliness like theirs.
At home once more,
They begin munching the young tufts of spring in the darkness.
I would like to hold the slenderer one in my arms,
For she has walked over to me
And nuzzled my left hand.
She is black and white,
Her mane falls wild on her forehead,
And the light breeze moves me to caress her long ear
That is delicate as the skin over a girl's wrist.
Suddenly I realize
That if I stepped out of my body I would break
Into blossom.

ODE TO THE AMOEBA   by Arthur Guiterman

Recall from Time's abysmal chasm
That piece of primal protoplasm
The First Amoeba, strangely splendid,
From whom we're all of us descended.
That First Amoeba, weirdly clever,
Exists today and shall forever,
Because he reproduced by fission;
He split himself, and each division
And subdivision deemed it fitting
To keep on splitting, splitting, splitting;
So, whatsoe'er their billions be,
All, all amoebas still are he.
Zoologists discern his features
In every sort of breathing creatures,
Since all of every living species,
No matter how their breed increases
Or how their ranks have been recruited,
From him alone were evoluted.
King Solomon, the Queen of Sheba
And Hoover sprang from that amoeba;
Columbus, Shakespeare, Darwin, Shelley
Derived from that same bit of jelly.
So famed he is and well-connected,
His statue ought to be erected,
For you and I and William Beebe
Are undeniably amoebae!

TARPON

by

Laurence   Lieberman

Section 12

Five shadows in heavy motion, lumbering half-seen,
　　　pass me on either side, shark
panic slowly leaving my fluttered breath pumping as I make

　　　out the Tarpons' armored plate scales,
diamonded in silvery weave, the undershot bulldog
　　　jaw, his thick cylindrical body,

a wingless fuselage, famed for muscling twelve foot
　　　leaps in the air on his tail's pole
vault—when hooked, and broadjumping thirty feet at a bolt,

PAUL KLEE *The Seafarer*

many times, in Kodak-flash succession.
Now some thirty tarpon pass, in clusters of three to six.
Still mindful of shark fins, I half-spin

radially, peering from side to side, with metronomic
evenness of rhythm, kicking to and fro
to sustain a stable axis of pivot, the only way to keep

from drifting blindly out of shore's safe
keeping, my attention fastened undivertedly to the man-sized
passersby. I scrutinize the larger specimens,

ruling out the offchance of a lone predator, prowling.
I take heart finally, as the school thins
out, a few last (three foot!) small fry trailing behind,

solitarily, one pausing just under my legs,
looking after the others, and up at me disconcertedly,
finally edging up to my spear for a closer

view . . . a being more innocent, quiet, curious—more frail
than myself. My hand, before my very eyes,
puts down claws: all the violence I so dreaded to find,

moments before, in a fancied pursuer, now
surging in my arm, up my back and neck, and finally,
shaking my eyes in my skull like false

teeth in a cup, I hang back. The loaded speargun,
its three rubbers taut for release,
jiggles between us, seemingly playful, fish-chumming

away the tarpon's caution, a kinship
springing up between us; my hand still shaking its fury,
become a strange brute thing, self-motived,

disengaged, yet clinging still to my wrist, tugging
at my joints as a mad dog on a leash,
yearning for a sickening engagement: *my eyes fix*

on a point above his head, drilling in.
A brain shot would yank him up, so much limp flesh
hung on a spit; a tail shot implode

all fierceness inside him, our two nerve cords thrown
into a queer freedom of naked contact,
as though our bodies had fallen away, and the nerves

danced and leapt and wound about each
other like quivering vines . . . . I have been here before.
I have dreamed the death of friends, died

in a friend's dream, and come back. For love, I could
kill, or be killed. I'll always return,
as a fish perhaps, as myself turned fish. Fish-friend,

I drop my spear. All terror, love, thee
I spare, who can tow a twenty foot sailing smack
for hours, or twist and snap a heavy

duty wrought iron spear like a pretzel, or tug
an ill-fated spearfisherman to breathless lung-forfeiting depths . . . In seconds flat.

by Robert Hayden

THE DIVER

Sank through easeful
azure. Flower
creatures flashed and
shimmered there—
lost images
fadingly remembered.
Swiftly descended
into canyon of cold
nightgreen emptiness.
Freefalling, weightless
as in dreams of
wingless flight,
plunged through infra-
space and came to
the dead ship,
carcass that swarmed with
voracious life.
Angelfish, their
lively blue and
yellow prised from
darkness by the
flashlight's beam,
thronged her portholes.
Moss of bryozoans
blurred, obscured her
metal. Snappers,
gold groupers explored her,
fearless of bubbling
manfish. I entered
the wreck, awed by her silence,
feeling more keenly
the iron cold.

With flashlight probing
fogs of water
saw the sad slow
dance of gilded
chairs, the ectoplasmic
swirl of garments,
drowned instruments
of buoyancy,
drunken shoes. Then
livid gesturings,
eldritch hide and
seek of laughing
faces. I yearned to
find those hidden
ones, to fling aside
the mask and call to them,
yield to rapturous
whisperings, have
done with self and
every dinning
vain complexity.
Yet in lanquid
frenzy strove, as
one freezing fights off
sleep desiring sleep;
strove against the
cancelling arms that
suddenly surrounded
me, fled the numbing
kisses that I craved.
Reflex of life-wish?
Respirator's brittle
belling? Swam from
the ship somehow;
somehow began the
measured rise.

THE RIVER

The lifeguard's whistle organized our swimming
Around the anchored raft at summer camp,
Saving us from the tricky channel current.
When he blew it, we gave in to the system,
Each raising his buddy's hand in the sudden quiet
To be reckoned, officially, among the living.
Half a pair meant someone might have drowned
Or, more likely, not checking out, gone back
To his cabin where no one made him buddy,
Where, if he wished, he could desert the raft,
The restricting whistle, all practiced safety,
And, dreaming the channel's bottom, sound
That deep cut, the rock's dark hollows, and the cold.

I have been back once, when no one was there,
And poked around in the empty cabins
Boarded against vandals as if something valuable
Were left to steal, where no one was dreaming.
Yet, as if in a dream, I saw a name
The same as mine printed in fading chalk
On a wall, and I took a dented canteen
With a torn case from a nail rusted with rain.

It lay on the beach with my clothes while I went swimming   by Dabney Stuart
Where the channel cuts deep across from the steady raft,
Without a buddy. In over my head,
I finned to the bottom, expelling breath
Until the cold pressure cracked in my ears,
Then fought that pressure upwards with my arms
And shot, like a dolphin, high
Into the weightless air
Over and over again, each time higher,
Until I could use the bottom as a springboard.
However high I went, there was always bottom.

After, I took the canteen to the springs
Which feed the river, and filled it.
It hangs now on a nail in my room,
And when the season's dry and the city liquid
Tastes too much of metal and the system
That pumps it to my taps,
I drink that water, and find it cool and clear.

BY

THE

SWIMMING

by

Robert

Sward

By the swimming
The sand was wetter
The farther down you dug; I dug:
My head and ear on top
Of the sand, my hand felt water. . .
And the lake was blue not watching.
The water was just waiting there
In the sand, like a private lake.
And no one could kick sand
Into my digging, and the water
Kept going through my fingers slow
Like the sand, and the sand was water too.
And then the wind was blowing everyplace,
And the sand smelled like the lake,
Only wetter. It was raining then:
Everybody was making waxpaper noises,
And sandwiches, kicking sand
And running with newspapers on their heads;
Baldmen and bathinghat-ladies, and nakedpeople.
And all the sand turned brown and stuck together
Hard: and the sky was lightning, and the sun
Looked down sometimes to see how dark it was
And to make sure the moon wasn't there.
And then we were running: and everybody was under
The hotdog-tent eating things, spitting very mad
And waiting for the sky, and to go home.

DEPOT IN A RIVER TOWN

by Miller Williams

In the depot and the darkened day
the clack of an old pinball machine
demands a curious notice.
More sleeping than not
a satchel faced farmer makes noises.
A sailor circles like a child in church.

In the depot and the darkened day
I surrender my back to the imperative bench,
unlistening hear the emphatic pencil
tap itself on the table.

The little blonde reads
and fingers the cloth of her blouse
like a nun telling beads.

Cracked across after an ancient painting
the face of the woman with children
ignores and ignores.
There is fog at the windows
and the open doors.

Within the ear's rim rises a separate sound.
Wood slapping side slipping water sounds
settle me deep.
I feel again the penny in my pocket
and the slow sleep of the river
wraps me round.

First, you think they are dead.
Then you are almost sure
One is beginning to stir.
Out of the crushed ice, slow
As the hands on a schoolroom clock,
He lifts his one great claw
And holds it over his head;
Now he is trying to walk.

But like a run-down toy;
Like the backward crabs we boys
Waded for in the creek,
Trapped in jars or a net,
And then took home to keep.
Overgrown, retarded, weak,
He is fumbling yet
From the deep chill of his sleep

As if, in a glacial thaw,
Some ancient thing should wake
Sore and cold and stiff,
Struggling to raise one claw
Like a defiant fist,
Yet wavering, as if
Starting to swell and ache
With that thick peg in the wrist.

I should wave back, I guess.
But still in his permanent clench,
He's fallen back with the mass
Heaped in their common trench
Who stir, but do not look out
Through the rainstreaming glass,
Hear what the newsboys shout,
Or see the raincoats pass.

LOBSTERS IN

THE WINDOW

by

W. D. Snodgrass

THE CRABS

There was a bucket full of them. They spilled,
crawled, climbed, clawed; slowly tossed
and fell: precision made: cold iodine color of their own
world of sand and occasional brown weed, round stone
chilled clean in the chopping waters of their coast.
One fell out. The marine thing on the grass
tried to trundle off, barbarian and immaculate and to be
                                             killed
with his kin. We lit water: dumped the living mass
in: contemplated tomatoes and corn: and with the good
                                 cheer of civilized man,
cigarettes, that is, and cold beer, and chatter,
waited out and lived down the ten-foot-away clatter
of crabs as they died for us inside their boiling can.

Richmond   Lattimore

WILD WEST   by Robert Boylan

Now let us speak of cowboys who on swift
White horses over blue-black deserts sped,
Their pistols blazing and their proud blood shed
In paint-flecked shanties on the haunted cliffs
Or in the bars of ghost-towns. Let us tell
The legends of fierce heroes motherless,
Not Indians, not Easterners, whose quests
And daring deeds inscribed their names in hell.
Bravely they shot it out, did Wyatt Earp,
Billy the Kid, Bill Hickok, Jesse James.
Now what remains but moving-picture dreams
Of all that fury and fast villainy?
Lone cactuses where bullets spit and ripped
The courage of the eyelid from the eye?
A rusting stirrup and a rowel thrust
Up from the calcifying sun-baked dust
Where some unknown avenger fell to sleep?
A wind-blown piece of buckskin that looked grand
When it was stretched upon the living hip
Of him who lies now six feet under ground?
Cowboys were not immortal. All they did,
Guzzling and gunning, ended when they died.

Section 13

134

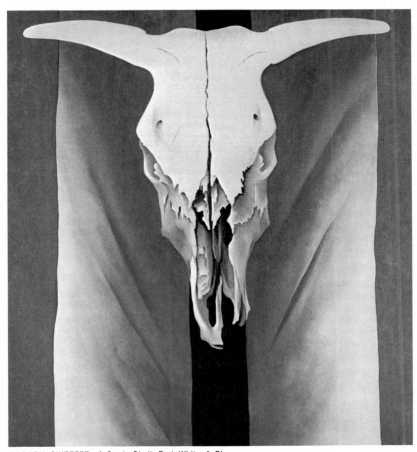

GEORGIA O'KEEFFE *A Cow's Skull: Red, White, & Blue*

RAIN OR HAIL

rain or hail
sam done
the best he kin
till they digged his hole

:sam was a man

stout as a bridge
rugged as a bear
slickern a weazel
how be you

(sun or snow)

gone into what
like all them kings
you read about
and on him sings

a whippoorwill;

E. E. Cummings

heart was big
as the world aint square
with room for the devil
and his angels too

yes,sir

what may be better
or what may be worse
and what may be clover
clover clover

(nobody'll know)

sam was a man
grinned his grin
done his chores
laid him down.

Sleep well

MY

OLD MAID

AUNT

by Dodi Schultz

My old maid aunt
angular and antiseptic
lived at a lethargic
edificial residential
hotel in Brooklyn
U.S.A. She ripened
reddened and patch-by-hair
shriveled in a steno's chair
and at fifty-five or -six
finally felt a
blooming inside her
but it turned out to be
intestinal cancer which
in fits and starts killed
her. At the wake
relatives regaled
each other with roses
traded paper tissues
and congratulated one
another upon the
astounding number of
featureless file clerks who
came respect-paying.
My old maid aunt
just lay there looking
tired and empty.

SUICIDE POND   by Kathy McLaughlin

It lay, dark in the corner of the field,
Deep and unclouded, like a devil's well,
The dank fern gathered round it in great clumps;
All the wild air was heavy with the smell
Of tansy; and it had the awful look
Of hidden and forbidden water. When
The seasons changed and winter dropped its cloud,
It did not dream in silver, but this fen
Remained a black hole gaping in the snow.
No stream led out of it, no stream led in;
No stars reflected in it; rumor said
Men plunged into its cold and took their sin,
Downing it with clenched hands and blinded eyes,
Far down the pitted water; and, alone
And trembling, we, when young, looked down and saw
Grim suicides in bottom-rock and stone.

ELEGY FOR A JAZZ MUSICIAN

(One of the

Mound City Blue Blowers)

Sound from hearing disconnects
In the room within the ground
Under the softly drumming rain.
He is not listening, who,
When all the rest are blowing blue,
Stroked a suitcase with a whiskbroom
For the soft effects.

Ernest Kroll

FABLE   by Merrill Moore

Does everyone have to die? *Yes, everyone.*
Isn't there some way I can arrange
Not to die—cannot I take some strange
Prescription that my physician might know of?

No. I think not, not for money or love;
Everyone has to die, yes, everyone.

Cannot my banker and his bank provide,
Like a trust fund, for me to live on inside
My warm bright house and not be put into
A casket in the clay, can they not do
That for me and charge a fixed per cent
Like interest or taxes or the rent?

No, Madame, I fear not, and if they could
There might be more harm in it than good.

James Wright

MUTTERINGS
OVER
THE CRIB
OF A
DEAF CHILD

"How will he hear the bell at school
Arrange the broken afternoon,
And know to run across the cool
Grasses where the starlings cry,
Or understand the day is gone?"

Well, someone lifting cautious brows
Will take the measure of the clock.
And he will see the birchen boughs
Outside the sagging dark from the sky,
And the shade crawling upon the rock.

"And how will he know to rise at morning?
His mother has other sons to waken,
She has the stove she must build to burning
Before the coals of the night-time die,
And he never stirs when he is shaken."

I take it the air affects the skin,
And you remember, when you were young,
Sometimes you could feel the dawn begin,
And the fire would call you, by and by,
Out of the bed and bring you along.

"Well, good enough. To serve his needs
All kinds of arrangements can be made.
But what will you do if his finger bleeds?
Or a bobwhite whistles invisibly
And flutes like an angel off in the shade?"

He will learn pain. And, as for the bird,
It is always darkening when that comes out.
I will putter as though I had not heard,
And lift him into my arms and sing
Whether he hears my song or not.

In the walled world of darkness and his fever
the chairs were beasts, the lamp-shade was a lowered head.
The sheet was an expanse of ice enfolding
the clenched fright and the weakness in the bed.

His malady that night was a deep forest
where danger stood like trees, or soldiers, and low cries
rose from his footsteps, and in all the shadows
presences lurked and stared with round green eyes.

CHILD WITH

MALARIA

He listened as the apes grew loud and bickered
in the next room, with cognac and cigars, and after
an interval he could not measure, heard
through the cold wall a burst of simian laughter.

As the apes cried beneath bright candelabra
he sailed far on the incandescent ship, alone,
and reeled with vertigo, and followed downward
the firmament of blood about the bone.

Four other nights rose and were populated
by rivers, priests, a conflagration and a ghost,
but afterward the circular warm tide
and the apes' voices he remembered most.

Clark Mills

140

OUT OF
BLINDNESS

Give names to sounds,
if it so please you:
call the abrupt tumultuous thrum
of gasoline explosion—"airplane."
But it is not.
It is noise obliterating bird-song.

Call wind among invisible leaves,
"rustling whisper of the trees."
But it is not.
It is an oval defined by silence,
wherein a multitude
of faint staccato clicks
sound magically.

Say—if you like—the weightless warm
against my cheek is sunlight,
and the cool my cheek feels
(penetrating yet leaving undisturbed
the film of warmth) is wind.
I will agree and we will play our game.
But do not ask me to believe
That *name* and *feel* are quite the same.

Your language of the sight is current coin
for our transaction, I agree.
But in my *real*
not seen things count
but sound and what I feel.
I link these, each to each
within the brain until—
though alien to your world—
my tongue can speak your speech to a degree
that buys me privilege of your company.

Leslie B. Blades

A SOLITUDE

A blind man. I can stare at him
ashamed, shameless. Or does he know it?
No, he is in a great solitude.

O, strange joy,
to gaze my fill at a stranger's face.
No, my thirst is greater than before.

In his world he is speaking
almost aloud. His lips move.
Anxiety plays about them. And now joy

of some sort trembles into a smile.
A breeze I can't feel
crosses that face as if it crossed water.

The train moves uptown, pulls in and
pulls out of the local stops. Within its loud
jarring movement a quiet,

the quiet of people not speaking,
some of them eyeing the blind man,
only a moment though, not thirsty like me,

and within that quiet his
different quiet, not quiet at all, a tumult
of images, but what are his images,

he is blind? He doesn't care
that he looks strange, showing
his thoughts on his face like designs of light

flickering on water, for he doesn't know
what *look* is.
I see he has never seen.

And now he rises, he stands at the door ready,
knowing his station is next. Was he counting?
No, that was not his need.

When he gets out I get out.
'Can I help you towards the exit?'
'Oh, alright.' An indifference.

But instantly, even as he speaks,
even as I hear indifference, his hand
goes out, waiting for me to take it,

142

and now we hold hands like children.
His hand is warm and not sweaty,
the grip firm, it feels good.

And when we have passed through the turnstile,
he going first, his hand at once
waits for mine again.

'Here are the steps. And here we turn
to the right. More stairs now.' We go
up into sunlight. He feels that,

the soft air. 'A nice day,
isn't it?' says the blind man. Solitude
walks with me, walks

beside me, he is not with me, he continues
his thoughts alone. But his hand and mine
know one another,

it's as if my hand were gone forth
on its own journey. I see him
across the street, the blind man,

and now he says he can find his way. He knows
where he is going, it is nowhere, it is filled
with presences. He says, *I am.*

Denise Levertov

HAY FOR THE HORSES

He had driven half the night
From far down San Joaquin
Through Mariposa, up the
Dangerous mountain roads,
And pulled in at eight a.m.
With his big truckload of hay
            behind the barn.
With winch and ropes and hooks
We stacked the bales up clean
To splintery redwood rafters
High in the dark, flecks of alfalfa
Whirling through shingle-cracks of light,
Itch of haydust in the
            sweaty shirt and shoes.
At lunchtime under Black oak
Out in the hot corral,
—The old mare nosing lunchpails,
Grasshoppers crackling in the weeds—
"I'm sixty-eight" he said,
"I first bucked hay when I was seventeen
I thought, that day I started,
I sure would hate to do this all my life
And dammit, that's just what
I've gone and done."

Gary Snyder

THE RANCHER

Hard old gray eyes, no pity
in him after years branding cattle—
a cruel man with cows & men

he drove both hard & once
when he was 70 tried to kill
a young puncher for smiling at his

old wife, sat down & cried in fury
because his grown sons took his
ivoryhandled .45 away, held

his head in his arms & didn't
ever come back to the dance.
After awhile his wife went slowly

out into the clear night
saying how late it is getting
now isn't it? without

pity for his eyes, him showing
nothing the next morning
barking at the hands to get

popping, the sun already up,
coffee on the fire & him
stifflegged, hard pot hanging

over the saddlehorn, he led
fall's last drive
across the hazy range.

Keith Wilson

Section 14

144

THE RAINWALKERS   by Denise Levertov

An old man whose black face
shines golden-brown as wet pebbles
under the streetlamp, is walking
two mongrel dogs of dis-
proportionate size, in the rain,
in the relaxed early-evening avenue.

The small sleek one wants to stop,
docile to the imploring soul of the trashbasket,
but the young tall curly one
wants to walk on; the glistening sidewalk
entices him to arcane happenings.

Increasing rain. The old bareheaded man
smiles and grumbles to himself.
The lights change: the avenue's
endless nave echoes notes of
liturgical red. He drifts

between his dogs' desires.
The three of them are enveloped—
turning now to go crosstown—in their
sense of each other, of pleasure,
of weather, of corners,
of leisurely tensions between them
and private silence.

FLORIDA ROAD WORKER   by Langston Hughes

I'm makin' a road
For the cars to fly by on,
Makin' a road
Through the palmetto thicket
For light and civilization
To travel on.

Sure,
A road helps everybody!
Rich folks ride—
And I get to see 'em ride.

I'm makin' a road
For the rich to sweep over
In their big cars
And leave me standin' here.

I ain't never seen nobody
Ride so fine before.
Hey, Buddy! Look!
I'm makin' a road.

A VALEDICTORY TO STANDARD OIL OF INDIANA

by David Wagoner

In the darkness east of Chicago, the sky burns over the
      plumbers' nightmares
Red and blue, and my hometown lies there loaded with
      gasoline.
Registers ring like gas-pumps, pumps like pinballs, pinballs like
      broken alarm clocks,
And it's time for morning, but nothing's going to work.
From cat-cracker to candle-shop, from grease-works along the
      pipeline,
Over storage tanks like kings on a checkerboard ready to jump
      the county,
The word goes out: With refined regrets
We suggest you sleep all day in your houses shaped like lunch
      buckets
And don't show up at the automated gates.
Something else will tap the gauges without yawning
And check the valves at the feet of the cooling-towers without
      complaining.
Standard Oil is canning my high school classmates
And the ones who fell out of junior high or slipped in the grades.
What should they do, gassed up in their Tempests and Comets,
      raring to go
Somewhere with their wives scowling in front and kids stuffed
      in the back,

Past drive-ins jammed like car-lots, trying to find the beaches
But blocked by freights for hours, stopped dead in their tracks
Where the rails, as thick as thieves along the lakefront,
Lower their crossing gates to shut the frontier? What can they
	think about
As they stare at the side of boxcars for a sign,
And Lake Michigan drains slowly into Lake Huron,
The mills level the Dunes, and the eels go sailing through the
	trout,
And mosquitoes inherit the evening, while toads no bigger than
	horseflies
Hop crazily after them over the lawns and sidewalks, and the
	rainbows fall
Flat in the oil they came from? There are two towns now,
One dark, one going to be dark, divided by cyclone fences;
One pampered and cared for like pillboxes and cathedrals,
The other vanishing overnight in the dumps and swamps like a
	struck sideshow.
As the Laureate of the Class of '44—which doesn't know it has
	one—
I offer this poem, not from hustings or barricades
Or the rickety stage where George Rogers Clark stood glued to
	the wall,
But from another way out, like Barnum's "This Way to the
	Egress,"
Which moved the suckers when they'd seen enough. Get out of
	town.

THE PRODUCE DISTRICT

by Thom Gunn

After the businesses had moved, before
The wrecking started
For the high-rise blocks:
An interim:
Whoever walked along these streets
Found it was shared with him
Only by pigeons, single or in flocks.

Where each night trucks had waited
By warehouse and worn ramp
With oranges or celery to unload,
Now it was smell of must, rot, fungus, damp.
The crumbling and decay accelerated,
Old mattresses and boards in heaps
Losing their colors with their shapes,
The smaller things
Blending like humus, on the road.
And silence—no, small creaks,
Small patterings,
While now, above, the thump and whirr of wings.
The pigeons, grey on grey,
In greater number
Than ever here before
Pecked round the rotting lumber,
Perched on the roofs and walls,
Or wheeled between the faded signs
And broken ornamental scrolls.

I watched the work of spiders, rats, and rain,
And turning onto Front Street found
I was not there alone.
He stood unmoving on the littered ground
In bright scrubbed denims
An airgun loosely in his hands
Staring at something overhead.

Shooting pigeons. I looked at his lined face,
Hard, ruddy, any age,
Cracking into a smile.
Short greying hair. He shrugged and said,
What's there to do on Sundays,
Sooner do this than booze.

I stood beside him while
He aimed at a parapet some forty-five yards off.
A bang. One pigeon as the others rose
A lump of fluff
Dropped from among them lightly to the street.
Cool air, high fog, and underfoot
Through soft mould, shapes felt like uneven root
Ridging a forest floor.
The place losing itself, lost now, unnamed,
Birds wheeling back, with a low threshing sound.
He aimed
And then once more
I heard the gun repeat
Its accurate answer to the wilderness,
Echoing it and making it complete.
The maple shoots pushed upwards through the ground.

THE MARKET MAN

The walnut brains think moist
in their light tan skulls;
the apples croon redly
of their tooth white pulp;
and the squash curves voluptuously
in its yellow skin.
It is cold and the market man
burns an orange crate;
it is dark and bare bulbs hang down
like fiery glass pears.
The market man has big blunt thumbs,
he feels chapped melons;
the market man has a strong mouth,
dry as potato dust;
the market man has black grape eyes,
no seeds show in them.
The market man has lonely shanks,
he splats lemons against a wall;
the market man is angry at the cold,
he strips the heads of lettuce down
and throws the green leaves on the cobble street;
the market man smells the salty river,
he bites an onion open with his teeth
and floods the black night with tears and burning.

John Ratti

THE

MISERY

OF

MECHANICS

*   *   *

by   Philip   Booth

The misery of mechanics, back
after Labor Day, with nothing

to punch but the Time Clock:
somebody's wife has a squeak

in her new right-rear door;
an old professor phones in

for his first State Inspection.
Dry-tongued with pushbutton

coffee, shapeless in cover-
alls, each of a thousand

mechanics, all over town,
pushes darkly in under

the oil pan, drained as he
elbows his creeper to work.

Repairing himself to sleep,
wrenching his nails with soapstone,

he washes his hands of Chevys,
zips carefully, and punches

out: Dodges are still
expensive, Fords too cheap

to be worth repair. Driving
the daily bridge from Mens' Room

to wife, he figures the whole
damn job, the complete over-

haul, at the usual flat rate:
bridges, marriages, used

car lots—his mechanic's
eye sees that the parts are all there;

it is, in fact, already jacked up.
But nothing that he can fix.

SALE

Went into a shoestore to buy a pair of shoes,
There was a shoe salesman humming the blues
Under his breath; over his breath
Floated a peppermint lifesaver, a little wreath.

I said please I need a triple-A,
And without stopping humming or swallowing his lifesaver away
He gave one glance from toe to toe
And plucked from the mezzanine the very shoe.

Skill of the blessed, that at their command
Blue and breathless comes to hand
To send, from whatever preoccupation, feet
Implacably shod into the perfect street.

Josephine   Miles

WHAT ARE THE MOST UNUSUAL THINGS

YOU FIND IN GARBAGE CANS?

(A journalist questions members of the Scavenger's Protective Association, Inc.)

by James Schevill

BURRISTREZZI

After a wedding or baby shower
I find
lots of gifts in the garbage.
What you don't like, you throw away,
I guess.
Sell it, you're a cheapskate,
Give it, you feel guilty,
So you chuck it in the garbage.

EDWARD KIENHOLZ *Ida Franger*

DUCKMANN

Bikes, baby cribs, brand new coats.
Big hotels are the best for clothing.
Family districts you don't see nothing
Too unusual. Lots of little stuff.
But hotels you hold your breath for
        chuck-offs.
People buy too much and stagger out,
        loaded.
They don't have no camels nowadays,
And planes don't carry all that stuff.
My dog sleeps in the baby crib.

BENSON

In the trash
  behind the old Hall of Justice
    once
      I found a wooden leg.

JONES

Plenty of girly pictures
    you know, gals
   stacked up to the sky;
you see one of them
    comin' at you
      in real life,
you'd take off
        zoom
    like a rocket.
But in a garbage can
   they don't smell so real.

FERRORE

I've found helmets, medals, and a bayonet
For my World War I collection. The bayonet's
The first kind they made where you stick it in,
Twist, and it don't come out without
Bringing half a guy's insides with it.
I like to take a war in the past.
The uniforms were more colorful,
And to wear those helmets you musta
Had a head as strong as a rock.
When you got a medal, they strung it
Real fruitcake on a rainbow ribbon.
You didn't just load your chest with
Little bars and flags like now.

SWINTON

I've got about twenty radios I found
All around my house, on the floor
    on shelves, in closets,
        on the bureau.

That way I make my own stereo.
Maybe I turn on four at the same time,
    or listen to different shows
        in different rooms.

News for breakfast in the kitchen
Music in the bathroom, baseball
    in the backyard with a beer
        politicians in the basement.

Sometimes I just turn 'em all off
And walk around quiet through the rooms.
    That's a good feeling too,
        looking at all those radios.

HANFORD

Picture frames. Pictures too, sometimes,
Landscapes mostly, cows, trees.
Once I found a picture of Jesus Christ.
I've got thirty picture frames at home,
All kinds of frames from plain to fancy.
I haven't bought one since I married.
Sometimes I just put 'em on the wall.
When there's nothing in the frame,
You can see the frame real good.

PAINTER

Cash
    wristwatches
    and a gold
        wedding ring

HAMILTON

Old books
  you never saw
    so many
      god damn
        old books
          with weird titles
        like
"Rebecca of Sunnybrook Farm"

BINDINI

The most unusual thing I ever found was
    an Espresso machine
It worked and I still use it in my home.
    Every morning with that coffee
    And you've got the stomach
    For a day with garbage.

FLIGHT   Steve Allen

You know the sitting on the train not-knowing feeling
As to which is moving, you or the station?
You can do it with the whole earth if you know how.
Give up? Stand by night in a silent snowfall, perhaps under
                                          a street lamp.
If the flakes are large and falling steadily and the wind
                                  has gone to bed
And you look straight up, eventually it is the flakes that
                are motionless, white blobs of paint on a canvas,
And you and the whole earth (which is magnetized to your
            feet bottoms) are floating softly, airily up.

The ride lasts only a few seconds because
Your "senses" intrude.
But it's lovely while it lasts. If you can take it
            come back and tell me.
I've almost forgotten.

MORRIS GRAVES *Wounded Scoter II*

SEAGULLS   by Frances Higginson Savage

Two medicos, immaculate in gray
Hold converse on the pilings of the quai.
Each eyes the other with a chilly glance,
As rivals will, of deep malevolence;
Each then propounds his learned diagnosis:
"Ulcer," screams one; the other shrieks, "Cirrhosis!"

Then, since the conference will not agree,
Professionally cool, they fly away.

TO A TIDELANDS OIL PUMP

Durable bird pulls interminable worm,
Coiled in subterranean caverns;
Feeds on fossils of fern and monsters.

No robin probes the stubborn burrow;
No blackbird grapples with the earth;
No sparrow draws the marrow from the land.

Hungry, iron-legged heron,
Stark against the apathetic stars
Or stare of sun or variable weather,
Wears no feathers, only barren pinions;
Stoic in steely skin.

In delicate steps across the sand
Fastidious piper picks his way;
Your grim proboscis dips and dips and dips
All night, all day.

Beatrice Janosco

THE HAWK

tilted while we sat still,
theoretic thing,
and streaked, bent tense to kill
on pointed wing—

what was a feathered cross
cruising admired in skies
became what we knew of hawks—
a clawed surprise

to tear whatever it was—
lamb tottering lost
or rabbit hopping in grass—
some gentleness,

as if nature had meant
to demonstrate by this
bird with a low intent,
its deadly purpose—

how meekness hasn't a chance
under the eye of power,
the high, wide cateyed glance
and hookbeak glower

of a hawk or anything else
so well equipped
with plumages of stealth,
sharply tipped.

So we thought as we watched
the hawk swoop down—
nothing is safe that's soft
or slow on the ground,

yet we had food for thought
when the hawk flapped up again—
tenderness hadn't been caught.
It blended in.

Harold Witt

BATS by Randall Jarrell

A bat is born
Naked and blind and pale.
His mother makes a pocket of her tail
And catches him. He clings to her long fur
By his thumbs and toes and teeth.
And then the mother dances through the night
Doubling and looping, soaring, somersaulting—
Her baby hangs on underneath.
All night, in happiness, she hunts and flies.
Her high sharp cries
Like shining needlepoints of sound
Go out into the night and, echoing back,
Tell her what they have touched.
She hears how far it is, how big it is,
Which way it's going:
She lives by hearing.
The mother eats the moths and gnats she catches
In full flight; in full flight
The mother drinks the water of the pond
She skims across. Her baby hangs on tight.
Her baby drinks the milk she makes him
In moonlight or starlight, in mid-air.
Their single shadow, printed on the moon
Or fluttering across the stars,
Whirls on all night; at daybreak
The tired mother flaps home to her rafter.
The others all are there.
They hang themselves up by their toes,
They wrap themselves in their brown wings.
Bunched upside-down, they sleep in air.
Their sharp ears, their sharp teeth, their quick sharp faces
Are dull and slow and mild.
All the bright day, as the mother sleeps,
She folds her wings about her sleeping child.

AT THE AIRPORT

by Howard Nemerov

Through the gate, where nowhere and night begin,
A hundred suddenly appear and lose
Themselves in the hot and crowded waiting room.
A hundred others herd up toward the gate,
Patiently waiting that the way be opened
To nowhere and night, while a voice recites
The intermittent litany of numbers
And the holy names of distant destinations.

None going out can be certain of getting there.
None getting there can be certain of being loved
Enough. But they are sealed in the silver tube
And lifted up to be fed and cosseted,
While their upholstered cell of warmth and light
Shatters the darkness, neither here nor there.

TAKE-OFF   by Peter Thorpe

He let go,
moving a racket
down the length of his mile-and-a-half concrete
farewell to Mother Earth, the faceless slabs
blinking, blurring, disappearing, till the black scabs
of oil and rubber blended and vanished
and he lifted sweet and clean and struck out
for always-autumned altitude,
the door of daystars,
the bird now less refractory,
shinnying along on a long string of sky,
the priceless, skyscraping engine
turning brightly through its fearful chemistry,
thrusting the farm-quilts down, out and away
till all around for miles and miles and miles
that faded map of Texas lay majestic
far and away under the exotic metal
hissing and hung from the ox-straps of heaven.

163

EGO

When I was on Night Line,
flying my hands to park
a big-bird B-29,
I used to command the dark:
four engines were mine

to jazz; I was ground-crew,
an unfledged pfc,
but when I waved planes through
that flight line in Tennessee,
my yonder was wild blue.

Warming up, I was hot
on the throttle, logging an hour
of combat, I was the pilot
who rogered the tower.
I used to take off a lot.

With a flat-hat for furlough
and tin wings to sleep on,
I fueled my high-octane ego:
I buzzed, I landed my jeep on
the ramp, I flew low.

When a cross-country hop
let down, I was the big deal
who signaled big wheels to stop.
That's how I used to feel.
I used to get all revved up.

Philip Booth

MALFUNCTION   by Richard E. Albert

He fell in a sweeping arc
From airplane to earth.

You could almost express it
In an equation:

Speed of the airplane minus
Force of the propblast,

Pull of gravity, speed and
Direction of wind,

The slight factor of his jump,
Thrust of leg muscle.

I did not witness his fall,
I was too far off,

Too busy trying to slip
Away from the trees,

Pulling the risers, watching
The scallops of silk

Ruffled above by the wind.
I heard distant shouts:

"Pull your reserve! Pull! Reserve!"
I looked below me,

Saw the earth, the discs of chutes
Sliding to the ground

Like cookies off a tin sheet.
After I landed

It was much too far to walk.
I saw men running,

But the trucks were parked this way.
I know he is dead,

Know we will talk about it
Riding in the trucks

Feeling wind in our faces.
By tonight I would

Describe what all will have seen
By then: he fell fast

Without a sound, like a rock
In a handkerchief;

I was close by when he hit,
Saw him bounce six feet.

Forgetting to drink a toast
We will press bottles

Against our faces and hands,
Clinging to coldness,

Reliving all but the slight
Factor of his death.

VAPOR TRAILS   by Gary Snyder

Twin streaks twice higher than cumulus,
Precise plane icetracks in the vertical blue
Cloud-flaked light-shot shadow-arcing
Field of all future war, edging off to space.

Young expert U.S. pilots waiting
The day of criss-cross rockets
And white blossoming smoke of bomb,
The air world torn and staggered for these
Specks of brushy land and ant-hill towns—

I stumble on the cobble rockpath,
Passing through temples,
Watching for two-leaf pine
        —spotting that design.

FIREWORKS   by Ernest Kroll

People in a field with light and noise
Startle the dark, and savage boys
Scrabble among tall legs for rocket sticks.
Showers of the pyrotechnics
Wink in smoke, trailing a storm
Above the trees, against the warm
Moon. Burnt powder and burnt hay.
A railroad flare makes hellish day
On scattered faces. Sparklers in the gloom,
Like candles in an attic room,
Wander in ghostly conclave. It's the Fourth.
Aurora borealis from the north
Moves down above the field and thunders
Finale. The sky shuts up those fiery wonders,
And heals without a sign of scars.
The old and slow explosion of the stars.

VACANT HOUSE

Beside the old earth-colored
adobe house haphazard on the ground
whose doors have vanished
and whose window frames are empty
wherein tumbleweeds have hidden at last
from the wind in corners

the rusty upside-down cars
lie like dark wing-folded shells
of beetles on the dry earth.

Majestic cottonwoods
rise above the corral
with no boy to throw a rope
over a low-hanging branch,
no man to lean a rake
against the great trunk,
no woman to stand in the shade,
her apron fluttering as she holds
a hand over her eyes
against the brilliance.

The echo of horses stamping
has long ago faded from the air
and now only the crows
perch high in the upper boughs
to scold the ghosts
of those who once were here
working, belonging.

Jeanne DeL. Bonnette

Section 16

VARIATIONS FOR TWO PIANOS

For Thomas Higgins, pianist

There is no music now in all Arkansas.
Higgins is gone, taking both his pianos.

Movers dismantled the instruments, away
Sped the vans. The first detour untuned the strings.

There is no music now in all Arkansas.

Up Main Street, past the cold shopfronts of Conway,
The Brash, self-important brick of the college,

Higgins is gone, taking both his pianos.

Warm evenings, the windows open, he would play
Something of Mozart's for his pupils, the birds,

There is no music now in all Arkansas.

How shall the mockingbird mend her trill, the jay
His eccentric attack, lacking a teacher?

Higgins is gone, taking both his pianos.
There is no music now in all Arkansas.

Donald Justice

IF ALL THE UNPLAYED PIANOS

If all the unplayed pianos in America—
  The antimacassared uprights in old ladies' parlors
  In the storehouses the ones that were rented for vaudeville
  The ones where ill fame worsened and finally died
  The ones too old for Sunday-School helplessly dusty
  The ones too damp at the beach and too dry in the mountains
  The ones mothers used to play on winter evenings
  The ones silenced because of the children growing away—
Resounded suddenly all together from coast to coast:
Untuned joy like a fountain jetted everywhere for a moment:
The whole nation burst to untapped, untrammeled song:
It would make—in short—a most satisfactory occasion,
A phenomenon which the scientists could never explain.

Winfield Townley Scott

MOVING

Bookshelves empty, tables lampless, walls
bare, the house is a rubble of moving—
foothills of boxes, trunks
under clouds of ceiling.

           My friends
said good-bye hours ago, when June twilight
hung on the hills. Now, in late dark
muggy for stars, moths whir at the yellow porch light,
ping screens. By the one dim floor lamp
among the shadowy undoings of my life,
in a limbo between having gone and having gone,
I sit like a caretaker of my doom.
Not an ashtray or a spoon.
In the real dawn, I will be going.

My friends are sleeping, turned toward
tomorrows without me—will still be sleeping
when I begin to drive the familiar streets and roads
in which sun will come only after me.
If I called them now, in this hollow
past midnight, anything I said would
be from the future.

           Alone in the present,
I wait, smoking (a tin can for ashes).
Bugs thwack on the screens. Beyond love
I am a projectile into the future—
still hours, days away.
Time has stopped at the speed I am going, landmarks
appear strangely in new light,
clouds whirling past me, into the past.

The phone has been disconnected.
                          by Robert Wallace

EDWARD HOPPER   *Rooms by the Sea.*   Yale University Art Gallery, Bequest of Stephen Carlton Clark, B.A. 1903.

LOOKING

IN

THE

ALBUM

Here the formal times are surrendered
to the camera's indifferent gaze: weddings,
graduations, births and official portraits taken
every ten years to falsify appearances.
Even snapshots meant to gather afternoons
with casual ease are rigid. Smiles
are too buoyant. Tinny laughter echoes
from the staged scene on an artificial
beach. And yet we want to believe
this is how it was: That children's hair
always bore the recent marks of combs;
that trousers, even at picnics, were always
creased and we traveled years with the light
but earnest intimacy of linked hands or arms
arranged over shoulders. This is the record
of our desired life: Pleasant, leisurely on vacations,
wryly comic before local landmarks, competent
auditors of commencement speakers, showing
in our poses that we believed what we were told.
But this history contains no evidence
of aimless nights when the wilderness of ourselves
sprang up to swallow the outposts of what
we thought we were. Nowhere can we see
tears provoked by anything but joy. There
are no pictures of our brittle, lost intentions.
We burned the negatives that we felt did not give a true
account and with others made this abridgement of our lives.

Vern Rutsala

MEMORANDA   by William Dickey

The scars take us back to places we have been,
Cities named Masochism or Inaccuracy.
This little one between the finger and the thumb
Is something that my brother did to me
On a hot Washington's Birthday in the past,
When we were young and cruelly competent;
In a miniature world like a glass fishing float
He was the total image of intent.

Who stuck the pencil point into my palm?
It was so long ago that I cannot say;
But the black stick of graphite under the skin—
Some friend, some enemy put it there that way
To succeed in calling himself always to mind.
Action has consequence, and though his face
Has faded into the city of the lost,
I look at my hand and see the injured place.

Like hasty marks on an explorer's chart:
This white stream bed, this blue lake on my knee
Are an angry doctor at midnight, or a girl
Looking at the blood and trying not to see
What we both have seen. Most of my body lives,
But the scars are dead like the grooving of a frown,
Cannot be changed, and ceaselessly record
How much of me is already written down.

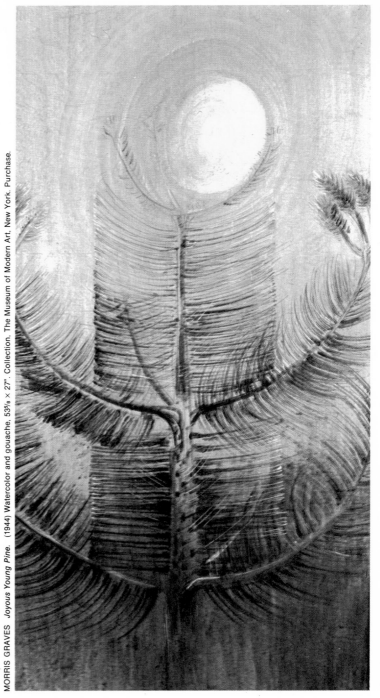

MORRIS GRAVES *Joyous Young Pine.* (1944) Watercolor and gouache, 53⅜ × 27″. Collection, The Museum of Modern Art, New York. Purchase.

Section 17

DAVID   by Earle Birney

I

David and I that summer cut trails on the Survey,
All week in the valley for wages, in air that was steeped
In the wail of mosquitoes, but over the sunalive weekends
We climbed, to get from the ruck of the camp, the surly

Poker, the wrangling, the snoring under the fetid
Tents, and because we had joy in our lengthening coltish
Muscles, and mountains for David were made to see over,
Stairs from the valleys and steps to the sun's retreats.

Our first was Mount Gleam. We hiked in the long afternoon
To a curling lake and lost the lure of the faceted
Cone in the swell of its sprawling shoulders. Past
The inlet we grilled our bacon, the strips festooned

On a poplar prong, in the hurrying slant of the sunset.
Then the two of us rolled in the blanket while round us the cold
Pines thrust at the stars. The dawn was a floating
Of mists till we reached to the slopes above timber, and won

To snow like fire in the sunlight. The peak was upthrust
Like a fist in a frozen ocean of rock that swirled
Into valleys the moon could be rolled in. Remotely unfurling
Eastward the alien prairie glittered. Down through the dusty

Skree on the west we descended, and David showed me
How to use the give of shale for giant incredible
Strides. I remember, before the larches' edge,
That I jumped a long green surf of juniper flowing

Away from the wind, and landed in gentian and saxifrage
Spilled on the moss. Then the darkening firs
And the sudden whirring of water that knifed down a fern-hidden
Cliff and splashed unseen into mist in the shadows.

III

One Sunday on Rampart's arête a rainsquall caught us,
And passed, and we clung by our blueing fingers and bootnails
An endless hour in the sun, not daring to move
Till the ice had streamed from the slate. And David taught me

How time on a knife-edge can pass with the guessing of fragments
Remembered from poets, the naming of strata beside one,
And matching of stories from schooldays. . . . We crawled astride
The peak to feast on the marching ranges flagged

By the fading shreds of the shattered stormcloud. Lingering
There it was David who spied to the south, remote,
And unmapped, a sunlit spire on Sawback, an overhang
Crooked like a talon. David named it the Finger.

That day we chanced on the skull and the splayed white ribs
Of a mountain goat underneath a cliff, caught tight
On a rock. Around were the silken feathers of kites.
And that was the first I knew that a goat could slip.

IV

And then Inglismaldie. Now I remember only
The long ascent of the lonely valley, the live
Pine spirally scarred by lightning, the slicing pipe
Of invisible pika, and great prints, by the lowest

Snow, of a grizzly. There it was too that David
Taught me to read the scroll of coral in limestone
And the beetle-seal in the shale of ghostly trilobites,
Letters delivered to man from the Cambrian waves.

V

On Sundance we tried from the col and the going was hard.
The air howled from our feet to the smudged rocks
And the papery lake below. At an outthrust we balked
Till David clung with his left to a dint in the scarp,

Lobbed the iceaxe over the rocky lip,
Slipped from his holds and hung by the quivering pick,
Twisted his long legs up into space and kicked
To the crest. Then grinning, he reached with his freckled wrist

And drew me up after. We set a new time for that climb.
That day returning we found a robin gyrating
In grass, wing-broken. I caught it to tame but David
Took and killed it, and said, "Could you teach it to fly?"

VI

In August, the second attempt, we ascended The Fortress.
By the forks of the Spray we caught five trout and fried them
Over a balsam fire. The woods were alive
With the vaulting of mule-deer and drenched with clouds all the morning,

Till we burst at noon to the flashing and floating round
Of the peaks. Coming down we picked in our hats the bright
And sunhot raspberries, eating them under a mighty
Spruce, while a marten moving like quicksilver scouted us.

VII

But always we talked of the Finger on Sawback, unknown
And hooked, till the first afternoon in September we slogged
Through the musky woods, past a swamp that quivered with frog song
And camped by a bottle-green lake. But under the cold

Breath of the glacier sleep would not come, the moonlight
Etching the Finger. We rose and trod past the feathery
Larch, while the stars went out, and the quiet heather
Flushed, and the skyline pulsed with the surging bloom

Of incredible dawn in the Rockies. David spotted
Bighorns across the moraine and sent them leaping
With yodels the ramparts redoubled and rolled to the peaks
And the peaks to the sun. The ice in the morning thaw

Was a gurgling world of crystal and cold blue chasms,
And seracs that shone like frozen saltgreen waves.
At the base of the Finger we tried once and failed. Then David
Edged to the west and discovered the chimney; the last

Hundred feet we fought the rock and shouldered and kneed
Our way for an hour and made it. Unroping we formed
A cairn on the rotting tip. Then I turned to look north
At the glistening wedge of giant Assiniboine, heedless

Of handhold. And one foot gave. I swayed and shouted.
David turned sharp and reached out his arm and steadied me
Turning again with a grin and his lips ready
To jest. But the strain crumbled his foothold. Without

A gasp he was gone. I froze to the sound of grating
Edge-nails and fingers, the slither of stones, the lone
Second of silence, the nightmare thud. Then only
The wind and the muted beat of unknowing cascades.

VIII

Somehow I worked down the fifty impossible feet
To the ledge, calling and getting no answer but echoes
Released in the cirque, and trying not to reflect
What an answer would mean. He lay still, with his lean

Young face upturned and strangely unmarred, but his legs
Splayed beneath him, beside the final drop,
Six hundred feet sheer to the ice. My throat stopped
When I reached him, for he was alive. He opened his gray

Straight eyes and brokenly murmured "over . . . over."
And I, feeling beneath him a cruel fang
Of the ledge thrust in his back, but not understanding,
Mumbled stupidly, "Best not to move," and spoke

Of his pain. But he said, "I can't move. . . . If only I felt
Some pain." Then my shame stung the tears to my eyes
As I crouched, and I cursed myself, but he cried,
Louder, "No, Bobbie! Don't ever blame yourself.

I didn't test my foothold." He shut the lids
Of his eyes to the stare of the sky, while I moistened his lips
From our water flask and tearing my shirt into strips
I swabbed the shredded hands. But the blood slid

From his side and stained the stone and the thirsting lichens,
And yet I dared not lift him up from the gore
Of the rock. Then he whispered, "Bob, I want to go over!"
This time I knew what he meant and I grasped for a lie

And said, "I'll be back here by midnight with ropes
And men from the camp and we'll cradle you out." But I knew
That the day and the night must pass and the cold dews
Of another morning before such men unknowing

The ways of mountains could win to the chimney's top.
And then, how long? And he knew . . . and the hell of hours
After that, if he lived till we came, roping him out.
But I curled beside him and whispered, "The bleeding will stop.

You can last." He said only, "Perhaps. . . . For what? A wheelchair,
Bob?" His eyes brightening with fever upbraided me.
I could not look at him more and said, "Then I'll stay
With you." But he did not speak, for the clouding fever.

I lay dazed and stared at the long valley,
The glistening hair of a creek on the rug stretched
By the firs, while the sun leaned round and flooded the ledge,
The moss, and David still as a broken doll.

I hunched to my knees to leave, but he called and his voice
Now was sharpened with fear. "For Christ's sake push me over!
If I could move. . . . Or die. . . ."The sweat ran from his forehead,
But only his eyes moved. A kite was buoying

Blackly its wings over the wrinkled ice.
The purr of a waterfall rose and sank with the wind.
Above us climbed the last joint of the Finger
Beckoning bleakly the wide indifferent sky.

Even then in the sun it grew cold lying there. . . . And I knew
He had tested his holds. It was I who had not. . . . I looked
At the blood on the ledge, and the far valley. I looked
At last in his eyes. He breathed, "I'd do it for you, Bob."

IX

I will not remember how nor why I could twist
Up the wind-devilled peak, and down through the chimney's empty
Horror, and over the traverse alone. I remember
Only the pounding fear I would stumble on It

When I came to the grave-cold maw of the bergschrund . . . reeling
Over the sun-cankered snowbridge, shying the caves
In the névé . . . the fear, and the need to make sure It was there
On the ice, the running and falling and running, leaping

Of gaping greenthroated crevasses, alone and pursued
By the Finger's lengthening shadow. At last through the fanged
And blinding seracs I slid to the milky wrangling
Falls at the glacier's snout, through the rocks piled huge

On the humped moraine, and into the spectral larches,
Alone. By the glooming lake I sank and chilled
My mouth but I could not rest and stumbled still
To the valley, losing my way in the ragged marsh.

I was glad of the mire that covered the stains, on my ripped
Boots, of his blood, but panic was on me, the reek
Of the bog, the purple glimmer of toadstools obscene
In the twilight. I staggered clear to a firewaste, tripped

And fell with a shriek on my shoulder. It somehow eased
My heart to know I was hurt, but I did not faint
And I could not stop while over me hung the range
Of the Sawback. In blackness I searched for the trail by the creek

And found it. . . . My feet squelched a slug and horror
Rose again in my nostrils. I hurled myself
Down the path. In the woods behind some animal yelped.
Then I saw the glimmer of tents and babbled my story.

I said that he fell straight to the ice where they found him,
And none but the sun and incurious clouds have lingered
Around the marks of that day on the ledge of the Finger,
That day, the last of my youth, on the last of our mountains.

STAYING ALIVE   by David Wagoner

Staying alive in the woods is a matter of calming down
At first and deciding whether to wait for rescue,
Trusting to others,
Or simply to start walking and walking in one direction
Till you come out—or something happens to stop you.
By far the safer choice
Is to settle down where you are, and try to make a living
Off the land, camping near water, away from shadows.
Eat no white berries;
Spit out all bitterness. Shooting at anything
Means hiking further and further every day
To hunt survivors;
It may be best to learn what you have to learn without a gun,
Not killing but watching birds and animals go
In and out of shelter
At will. Following their example, build for a whole season:
Facing across the wind in your lean-to,
You may feel wilder,
And nothing, not even you, will have to stay in hiding.
If you have no matches, a stick and a fire-bow
Will keep you warmer,
Or the crystal of your watch, filled with water, held up to the
   sun
Will do the same, in time. In case of snow,

Drifting toward winter,
Don't try to stay awake through the night, afraid of
    freezing—
The bottom of your mind knows all about zero;
It will turn you over
And shake you till you waken. If you have trouble sleeping
Even in the best of weather, jumping to follow
The unidentifiable noises of the night and feeling
Bears and packs of wolves nuzzling your elbow,
Remember the trappers
Who treated them indifferently and were left alone.
If you hurt yourself, no one will comfort you
Or take your temperature,
So stumbling, wading, and climbing are as dangerous as
    flying.
But if you decide, at last, you must break through
In spite of all danger,
Think of yourself by time and not by distance, counting
Wherever you're going by how long it takes you;
No other measure
Will bring you safe to nightfall. Follow no streams: they run
Under the ground or fall into wilder country.
Remember the stars
And moss when your mind runs into circles. If it should rain,
Or the fog should roll the horizon in around you,
Hold still for hours
Or days, if you must, or weeks, for seeing is believing
In the wilderness. And if you find a pathway,
Wheel rut, or fence wire,
Retrace it left or right—someone knew where he was going
Once upon a time, and you can follow
Hopefully, somewhere,
Just in case. There may even come, on some uncanny
    evening,

A time when you're warm and dry, well fed, not thirsty,
Uninjured, without fear,
When nothing, either good or bad, is happening.
This is called staying alive. It's temporary.
What occurs after
Is doubtful. You must always be ready for something to
     come bursting
Through the far edge of a clearing, running toward you,
Grinning from ear to ear
And hoarse with welcome. Or something crossing and
     hovering
Overhead, as light as air, like a break in the sky,
Wondering what you are.
Here you are face to face with the problem of recognition.
Having no time to make smoke, too much to say,
You should have a mirror
With a tiny hole in the back for better aiming, for reflecting
Whatever disaster you can think of, to show
The way you suffer.
These body signals have universal meaning: If you are lying
Flat on your back with arms outstretched behind you,
You say you require
Emergency treatment; if you are standing erect and holding
Arms horizontal, you mean you are not ready;
If you hold them over
Your head, you want to be picked up. Three of anything
Is a sign of distress. Afterward, if you see
No ropes, no ladders,
No maps or messages falling, no searchlights or trails blazing,
Then chances are, you should be prepared to burrow
Deep for a deep winter.

SOME SHORT POEMS . . . . by William Stafford

AN ARGUMENT AGAINST THE EMPIRICAL METHOD

Some haystacks don't even have any needle.

THE LIMBS OF THE PIN OAK TREE

"Gravity—what's that?"

STAR GUIDES   Any star is enough
if you know what star it is.

KIDS   They dance before they learn
there is anything that isn't music.

    COMFORT   We think it is calm here,
or that the storm is the right size.

JOAN MIRO *Dog Barking at the Moon*

Index of Titles

Index of Authors

3 4 5 6 7 8 9 10 11 12 13 14 15   RM   70 71 72 73 74 75